Marlena Frick was born in Kingston upon Hull and educated in Bristol. She is a freelance writer and artist, now retired after a career in newspapers as a reporter for the *Yorkshire Post* and the *Daily Mail* and as a sub editor and feature writer for *The Scotsman* in Edinburgh, where she now lives.

Her previous publications are *All the Days of His Dying*, *A Mouthful of Aloes* and *The Homecoming*, which was made into a film by the French film director Henri Colpi and won the annual book award of the American National Association of Independent Schools.

Those Loved and Loving Faces
A Memoir

Marlena Frick

Those Loved and Loving Faces
A Memoir

Vanguard Press

VANGUARD PAPERBACK

© Copyright 2013
Marlena Frick

A CIP catalogue record for this title is
available from the British Library.

ISBN 978 1 84386 794 4

*Vanguard Press is an imprint of
Pegasus Elliot MacKenzie Publishers Ltd.*
www.pegasuspublishers.com

First Published in 2013

**Vanguard Press
Sheraton House Castle Park
Cambridge England**

Printed & Bound in Great Britain

To Wendy Lees

Sigmund Freud said, "We are never so defenceless against suffering as when we love, never so helplessly unhappy as when we have lost our loved object or its love." How painfully true that is but it is a faint heart that refuses to make itself vulnerable to love, for love and even the loss of it teaches us many lessons. Acceptance of grief takes time but we can learn to live again even without the ones we love beside us. We must live in their name, as fully as we can; taking great armfuls of what this world has to offer in the hope of some answers after death and in gratitude for our quite extraordinary luck in having been alive at the same time as they were. – *M.F.*

Jim was dying and I was enraged. How could he do this to me who loved him so? I grabbed him by the shoulders and shook him until the tumour rattled in his brain.

"Don't you dare quit on me!"

He was weeping. He who had always been so strong and silent. Sobbing now. And watching his blind eyes spilling tears, I felt crucified.

"Laney," he whispered. "Don't get on at me. I don't want to leave you. I can't help it. I worship you and have always worshipped you but now I have to go. There are too many problems. There is nothing the doctors can do. You must be brave. Don't look back. No regrets. Don't be afraid. There is nothing to be afraid of."

But my anguish would not be stilled. I sat frozen at the bedside, terrified of losing him and groping for words. Dear God, I loved him so. I wasn't ready to let him go. It was too soon, too soon.

The words burst out. Almost angry. "How can you tell me not to be afraid when I am losing you? I love you and love you and love you. I can't live without you. I won't. I don't want to."

"You'll go on, Laney. I want you to. You will find the strength. We have had something special. The memory of it will keep you strong. And, if it's allowed, I promise I shall haunt you."

I began to cry then and, flinging myself across his threadbare body, pressed my lips hard upon his. Our kisses were anguished, our desperate tongues rooting deeper than I could remember them ever having done. It was as if we would eat each other up, sucking and probing and reaching for a last confirming taste of life. His life. Mine.

Our Last Supper, I thought, and could hardly breathe for the weight that was on my heart.

* * *

He died in Spain, where we were on holiday, and was cremated in Granada. The crematorium, overlooking the fragrant gardens of the Alhambra, was sleeked with rain and straddled by a rainbow, one end in the palace grounds, the other in the snow-capped peaks behind the town. Jim's pathway to heaven, I thought.

His simple, disposable coffin with twelve red roses lay on a catafalque in the centre of a pretty rotunda, my prince of love inside being sent on his way, according to Spanish custom, with a pair of trousers, shirt and tie packed with him so that he would be presentable when he met his Maker.

Dazed and speechless, a dozen friends gathered around the coffin. They included my good friend Wendy, who lives in Spain and who had managed to get us the last 15-minute 'slot' at the crematorium before the weekend, and Jim's daughter Alison who had flown in from Edinburgh in time to say goodbye. There was no minister, no service, just our dejected little group with hands joined on the coffin lid, our wet coats, hastily dumped on nearby chairs, steaming in the warmth from the ovens on the floor below. I was in such a state I had forgotten to take off my plastic mac and was dripping water everywhere, including on the coffin: rain and tears and the offerings of a runny nose affronting its simple, full-length cross.

I stared mesmerised by the little pool of snot spreading on the lid. Then Wendy nudged my arm and I realised I was expected to say something. But what? I couldn't think let alone express what was in my heart. I was a blighted creature. Mind blown. Brain of stone. Tongue of lead. Words would not come. Here was a wound that would never heal. What good were words? The Lord's Prayer? Futile in the face of all this madness, this obscenity of a loving man and all the fruit buds of his body about to be cindered. How would I live now without the love that had brought me to full flower, that was the reason for my song?

Shakespeare's words came haltingly…

Let me not to the marriage of true minds
Admit impediments. Love is not love
Which alters when it alteration finds,
Or bends with the remover to remove.

Oh No! It is an ever-fixèd mark
That looks on tempests and is never shaken;
It is the star to every wandering bark
Whose worth's unknown although his height be taken.

Love's not Time's fool, though rosy lips and cheeks
Within his bending sickle's compass come;
Love alters not with his brief hours and week,
But bears it out ev'n to the edge of doom:
If this be error, and upon me proved,
I never writ, nor no man ever loved.

As the plangent strings of a guitar playing the adagio from Rodrigo's *Concierto de Aranjuez* echoed around the hall, we shared out the roses on the coffin and watched helpless and cut down to size as two men came to carry my darling away.

"I'll love you for always, Jim Ritchie!" I shouted after him. "Haunt me. Please haunt me."

And then he was gone. Steel doors closed in on him and shut him out of my life forever and I felt so tired I could hardly stand.

Supportive arms ushered me outside into a sudden burst of spring sunshine and I stood trembling on the crematorium steps, feeling like Saint Sebastian shot through with arrows. Someone said we should eat and I went along, although I don't remember where we went or what I ate, if anything. I only remember noticing that Alison was in the same zombie-like state that I was in and wanted so much to go over to her and hold her... hold a part of him who was lost to me forever. Well, at least he had left something of himself behind. She had his eyes and his hair and the same smiley mouth that perhaps in the future I would be able to see from time to time. She had never resented him for deserting her mother and running away with me. She knew how wretched he had been. "I was just glad he had grabbed his chance of happiness," she told me later.

After the lunch ordeal we all returned to the crematorium to collect what remained of Jim. I wasn't prepared for it. Hadn't given it a thought. So that when a crematorium assistant almost apologetically handed me a blue and white ceramic pot containing Jim's ashes I almost fainted. *What bloody cosmic sadist thought this one up?*

Flying home to Edinburgh with him reduced like that was the hardest thing I have ever done. Wounded almost to death myself, I sat numbly in my seat, cradling the pot in its navy cloth cover on my lap and inwardly screaming at this ghastly nullification of my loved one.

The contrast of having gone out to Spain with a vivacious, smiley-mouthed man and returning with him five weeks later as a pot of scourings was surreal. Almost too much to bear. Shocked silly and on the edge of losing it, I could get through the flight only by downing as many brandies as the hostess had time to bring me. This truly was a hurt beyond imagining. I would never resign myself to it, to this shutting away of loved ones in the dusty lockers of the earth or casting them to the uncaring winds.

A poem of Edna St Vincent Millay came to mind and kept swirling around in my head. She couldn't resign herself either to the shovelling away of loved ones into the dark, impervious earth, no matter how 'elegant' the roses that might spring from their remains.

That's the image that's so hard to take, the reduction to dust and splinters of bone of all that we ever held most precious. All our loved ones gone. To what end then all that energy and love, wit, intelligence, tenderness and laughter?

I felt sick at the obscenity of what lay in my lap.

* * *

Back at home with no Jim to connect to and no-one else I wanted to connect to, I wondered how long I would last. I felt cold and listless, almost calcified, and did little but lie in bed sobbing around the clock. When I did venture out it was to wander the streets in search of all the places we had been together, remembering how it was, what he had said, how he had looked. Sometimes I'd cradle his pot of ashes in my arms and hug and kiss it as I would a child. I'd open the lid and run my fingers through his dust as once I'd run them through his hair. One day I drank a teaspoonful of him in a little brandy.

Now you are part of me for ever, my darling.

I brooded darkly. Started drinking heavily. Spent too much time sprawled unseeing in front of the television set. I wandered from room to room calling Jim's name, leafed for hours through our photograph albums and repeatedly played his favourite CDs, rending my heart over Mahler's adagios, Tchaikovsky's Violin Concerto, the 'Liebestod', the music from *Schindler's List*. And I crucified myself again and again over a recording he'd made of himself singing from *La Bohème* and *Cav* and

Pag. His rich tenor voice echoed uncannily throughout the flat and intensified my pain, yet I kept on playing the music.

I knew I was drinking excessively but what did that matter now? Drinking too much, weeping too much, alone too much. So bloody what? I didn't know who I was or what I wanted to do. Nothing. That was the answer. It was all too late for anything and at 67 I was too old to make an effort. Even opening a book or newspaper was too much effort. And it was certainly too much effort to socialise. I rejected most invitations to friends' dinner parties, unable to face the chit-chat everybody seemed to think would be good for me.

One of the best places I found respite was the cinema. I found solace sitting where Jim had once sat and in being lost and anonymous in the dark. Other places good to hide in when I couldn't bear the thought of being at home were art galleries. On cold, wet days I haunted them, finding quiet corners where I could sit and pretend to be contemplating the paintings but in reality shut off in a cinder-grey limbo. I frequented them because while I didn't want to talk to anyone, I needed other human beings around me to remind me that I was one too.

But there were days when the sense of defeat was so overwhelming that I couldn't drag myself out of bed let alone off to a cinema or an art gallery. Then I would lie all day in frigid isolation contemplating the ceiling and wondering why it was too much to ask to have my life back again. Was it really so difficult for God to send my best pal back with all his clowning, his scurrilous humour, his loving companionship? A simple enough thing for an Almighty God to do, one would think.

But no miracles were forthcoming from that direction and the gulf in my life widened and deepened. *Who shall I hug and kiss now, Jim Ritchie? Who will hug and kiss me? Who is there now to slip me a handkerchief when I am weeping at a movie? Who will be ready now with a sweet when I begin to cough during a concert at the Usher Hall? Who will tint my hair now?*

Scrub my back in the bath? Paint my toenails? Peel my apples? Empty the mousetraps? Bring me flowers? Cook supper when I am weary? Help with the ironing? Come up with a plastic bag to cover my hair when I am caught in the rain? Who will find my specs now when I lose them? Dress up as Santa Claus at Christmas? Keep cavy when I am caught short and have to dive into the nearest bushes? Who will suck my nipples, now, Jim Ritchie? Kiss my clit? Be there. Always. In my corner?

I pined for him, yearned to have it all back the way it was... to be with him twenty-four hours a day and able to kiss him whenever I felt like it, to watch him padding naked around the house, hear him testing the bathroom acoustics, see him fast asleep on the sofa, his specs slipped down his nose, his newspaper on the floor, watch him in his butcher's apron happily frying our fish supper to a frazzle, tumble again with him on the bed or in front of the fire, taste his sweet breath again in my mouth, the minty toothpaste on his tongue, have my nostrils filled with the scent of his patchouli, lick his ears the way I used to do. "Mummy Tiger," he'd say dreamily, just loving it.

How many times did we kiss, my love? I wish I'd kept count. Kisses every day, morning, noon and night and many times in between. And how many times did we swive, my ardent swain? How I wish I'd kept count of those times, too.

Darling, if I could have back all those kisses and caresses do you know what I would do with them? I'd plant them in a garden and wait to see what flowers sprang. Forget-me-nots for sure. And red roses and love-in-the-mist, sensuous, heavy-lidded peonies, flighty poppies, clamorous petunias and soft-mouthed pansies.

* * *

I was almost twenty-one when I was first introduced to love and eventually to all the pain and grief that are consequent upon it.

This cataclysmic event occurred early one morning on a snowy March day: air crisp and icy, azure sky cloud-stacked and luminous, brassy sun coruscating on snow-mantled trees and rooftops.

A trainee reporter on a Hull evening paper, I was chasing after a bus to get to a conference of arable farmers at the Station Hotel when I slipped on a patch of ice and fell.

Before I could get to my feet a man was at my side and helping me up. I had torn my stockings and blood was oozing from a gash on my right knee. We both stared dismayed at the damage.

"That's a nasty wound," he said. "We'd better get it cleaned. I am a doctor. I can patch it up for you. My surgery is just around the corner."

So off I went to get patched up – and was never the same again.

That day I took the first step along the road to the rest of my life. That day I was synchronised with my destiny. It needed only ten minutes in his company for me to know that this was the man I was going to marry.

Mieciu Frick was Polish and in practice with an old friend from his days at Warsaw University. I thought him dashing with a kind, quizzical face, a mobile mouth, impish green eyes and charcoal-coloured hair that flopped rakishly over his right brow. Just looking at him made me feel light-headed.

He winked at me as he cleaned my knee and laughing said: "Never run after boys or buses. There's always another one behind."

And that was it. Someone threw the crown of love out of heaven and it struck me like a rock, a radioactive rock. I felt my heart sizzling like a burger and steam coming out of my ears.

And as I blazed away from his surgery leaving a trail of melted footprints in the snow, I knew what it was that made the world go round and why poets got into such a tizzy about it.

I even attempted a few poems myself that week: poems about soaring on eagle's wings, being crowned with stars, kindled by lightning. All sorts of tosh. I was ecstatic, gyrostatic, throbbing with the bittersweet anguish of desire, deafened by the clamour of my blood and quite out of my mind with love; sick with it, too sick to eat or sleep or think of anything other than that a miracle had occurred and a Great Design accomplished in the universe.

My loss of direction, high colour and minimal appetite worried Aunt Alice with whom I was living.

"Is it my cooking? Something I've said?"

Grabbing her by her ample waist, I gave her a whirl.

"It's love, Al. I've just met the man I'm going to marry."

"Does he know this?"

"No. But I'm going back to tell him."

Which I did, telling him grandly: "We are meant for each other. I knew it as soon as I saw you. There was this great thump of recognition – like someone knocking on my heart – and I could hardly breathe for excitement."

I felt sheepish having said that. How stupid can you get? Never having been in love before how could I possibly know? There! He was laughing at me as I had known he would.

"Please don't laugh. This is important. I can't sleep for thinking about you, can't concentrate on work, can't eat …"

"I'm not laughing at you. Only taken by surprise. But you need not worry. It's nothing very serious. Only sex. I've sexually awakened you, that's all."

That's all? When I was turned upside down and inside out just looking at him?

"All I want is for you to take me in your arms," I said, wondering where this forward hussy had come from. Until then

21

I hadn't been interested in boys except as chums to play cricket or go cycling with, and fumbles behind the bicycle shed had left me cold. Now I was all hot for something I was only dimly aware of.

He looked slightly bemused but not indifferent.

"Perhaps we should talk about this over dinner."

I soared away, rocket-fuelled.

"He's right," Alice said when I reported back on the miraculous thing that had happened to me. "It is only sex. It's how we all feel the first time around. Think about it. How can it be love? Love grows between two people who have known each other a long time. You can't possibly love someone you know nothing about."

"Oh, but you can! I do! I do! My genes recognise him. We have known each other before."

She was laughing. "Oh dear! I'm not sure I can handle this metamorphosis."

I went to live with my Aunt Al after my parents' marriage broke up and they separated, my father running off to London with another woman, my mother going haywire for a year before settling down with someone else. It was a great relief to me to be free of them and away from the sounds of angry squabbling and my mother's tears. They were sounds that had long dogged my childhood and I can still vividly recall being five or six years old and sitting at the top of the stairs, listening scared and uncomprehending to the sounds of altercation below.

I understood later that it was all about the 'other women' in my father's life and I was sorry for my mother because she loved him. Later on, however, I didn't feel so sorry. Coming home early from school one afternoon I found her in bed with another man.

"What's sauce for the goose," she said defiantly. Maybe so, but that didn't help me. I was 13. Feeling I couldn't trust either of my parents I turned inwards and was lonely and troublesome at school, always having crushes on my women teachers, hoping they would notice me and love me as I thought I loved them.

Of my parents, my mother was the stronger, my father weak and vain. He was an Errol Flynn lookalike who could never resist a come-on from an attractive, preferably much younger, woman and because he was tall, blue-eyed and handsome and a big spender he got a lot of those. One of his groupies was a girl he used to saw in half during his conjuring act at the local pensioners' club and I remember hearing from Al how mother had gone to the club one night and tried to pull the girl's hair out. This made me cringe with shame.

I grew up learning from my mother all about his sexual exploits, his lies, the contraceptives in the bottom of his golf bag, the blonde hairs on his jacket, the scent of another woman, the lipstick stains on the front of his underpants. Although only dimly understanding the portent of all these things, I saw my mother's pain and, disgusted and disappointed, I shied away from my father and longed to leave home and be rid of both parents.

Mother, a leggy brunette with deep brown eyes and a great figure, was a dressmaker and fashion model when they met, my father a sales representative for a paint firm. They met at a dance. "Love at first sight," my mother said, and she still hankered after him even on her death bed thirty years later. "He was such a good lover," she sighed.

"He should have been," I snapped. "He was getting plenty of practice."

They both came from seafaring families, my paternal grandfather a tall, morose man who hardly ever spoke to me, was the skipper of a trawler out of Hull. It was only after his death that my grandmother discovered he had another wife and child in Stavanger, Norway. My other grandfather was a cook in the Merchant Navy. He came from a well-off family of money-lenders but because he preferred to go to sea rather than join the business, his father cut him out of the family. He was a jolly grandpa who dandled me on his knee, sang funny songs, read me stories and brought me interesting souvenirs from his travels, things like a necklace of shark's teeth, an elephant's foot, and bracelets made from exotic seeds. When he came home from sea he was usually tipsy and would go around the house hiding his money behind the pictures on the walls, in vases or in the piano. My grandmother always found it.

She was a strict woman, tall and aloof and with a strong sense of propriety. She came from a family of farmers in Lincolnshire and had been a lady's maid, which had given her a strong sense of conformity. All she worried about was what the neighbours would say so that when she learned her unmarried daughter was pregnant there was hell to pay and she turned her out of the house.

My paternal grandmother had a room to spare and, after I was born, my parents married and we all went to live in a small terraced house with a large black kitchen range where my mother baked bread and scones and, in the kitchen outhouse where we had our baths in a large tin bath, a copper boiler for heating water and a dolly tub and mangle which she used on wash days. There was a privy attached to the outhouse and a coal shed and beyond it a walled garden with a pocket handkerchief-sized patch of lawn where I used to play.

When my father was promoted to Head of Sales Department we started to rise in the world and the houses got bigger, with real gardens and indoor lavatories and proper baths. And then the Second World War broke out and my father joined the RAF and was posted to Bristol where he manned barrage balloons over Avonmouth docks. Mother and I went to Bristol to be near him. I got my 11plus there and won a place at a posh girls' school while mother got work in a grocery store in order to get us some extra food rations. With these and the apples and eggs I used to steal from a nearby farm we did quite well for apple pies and omelettes, although the egg raids came to a stop the day I brought home fleas from the hen house.

After the war, my brother Tim was born and father opened a paint and hardware store and started making money, lots of it, not just in the shop but organising deliveries of black market coal and anything else he could lay his hands on. I remember the police coming for him and he disappeared from our lives for 18 months. He had been sent to an open prison, not so much for the blackmarketeering, for the others who had been in on it with him were only fined, but for being, as the judge said, "An outrageous liar."

In prison he 'got religion' and wrote remorseful letters to my mother who, in the meantime, had packed up and moved us back to Hull to be near her family. In Hull, I messed around for a year on the house magazine of Reckitt and Colman and then got myself a job as a rookie reporter on the evening paper. Journalism was something I had always wanted to do from the age of 11 or 12 when I wrote short stories about the Black Hand Gang, which were greeted with much hilarity by all and sundry when I read them aloud on the top deck of the bus going home from school.

When the 'con' returned from the cooler he opened another hardware store and also a florist's which mother ran for him. He bought a third share in a racehorse that never got anywhere and a pair of shocking pink tweed plus fours with a matching jacket that mother refused to be seen with, and we moved to a rambling detached mock-Tudor house set in a wildly overgrown garden with apple and plum trees, a large raspberry patch and a small stream running through. Father had ditched Jesus by this time, but seemed to have settled and happiness and contentment and some semblance of normality appeared within reach of us all. For a few years it was …

And then the bastard ran off to London with mother's best friend, a brassy, hatchet-faced widow who looked as if she might be into a bit of S & M, which is the only reason I can think of for his dumping my vibrant, good-looking mother.

Not surprisingly, mother went to pieces. She was only 48 and panicked at being on the shelf. For months she was out clubbing and pubbing and dancing, sometimes until close on dawn, while Tim and I lay restless in our beds listening for the slam of the front door to tell us she was safely home.

It was a great relief to us both when a year later she met an antiques dealer who cared for her and together they set up in a pub in a pretty North Yorkshire village, taking Tim to live with them while I shacked up with Aunt Alice.

My aunt lived in a three-storey Georgian terrace house in Cottingham, on the outskirts of Hull and within easy commuting distance of my office. It was a roomy, rackety house of red brick with green shutters, four bedrooms, a book-lined study and a large sunny studio across the top floor from where, gins and tonics in hand, we watched Turneresque sunsets over the River Humber.

Al was an abstract painter and owner of a small gallery and art supply shop in the city centre. She was divorced, although amicably she said, her husband John having discovered after three years of marriage a preference for the gay life.

"I was so relieved when he wanted out," she confessed. "He was more interested in getting into my dresses than into my knickers and broadminded as I am, I found that a bit too much to take."

She looked every inch the eccentric artist that she was: built like a Valkyrie and with a penchant for flowing kaftans in vivid colours, junk jewellery and bright georgette scarves around her dyed Titian red hair.

She had a good head for business and could paint like a dream but housework and cooking were not her strong points so we had Mrs MacDonald, the gardener's wife, to keep house for us and see that we ate properly. If she hadn't been around to look after us we'd have lived on baked beans and Chardonnay – Al's culinary limit. That wouldn't have bothered me much. Life was too interesting to worry about eating. There was always something going on, people dropping in for poker nights, parties, croquet on the lawn, barbecues, Al's exhibitions to prepare for, piles of oranges to peel for her home-made orange brandy, sloes to pick for her speciality gin. Then there were weekends at Robin Hood's Bay, chipping away at rocks looking for ammonites, bird-watching on the high white cliffs at Flamborough Head and days messing about with paints in the studio where Al taught me about colour, shape and texture and how to look beneath the surface of the landscape for the spirit of place. She said I painted well and urged me to consider Art College but my heart was set on becoming the First Lady of Fleet Street, an ambition that was thwarted by my friend Jean Rook who got there first. However, there were no hard feelings because by that time I had been sidelined by Cupid.

After John's unmourned departure there was a lively parade of lovers through the house, Al passing from one to the other even before I could remember their names. One was a cheery, wild-haired sculptor with a penchant for sculpting women's breasts in their various shapes and sizes; another was a test pilot who was a bit of a comedian and boring with it; then there was a black actor doing a stint at Theatre in the Round, Scarborough, and a dab hand at chicken calypso and key lime pie; a farmer who kept us supplied with pheasant and grouse; and a cinema manager who was my favourite because I got to see his movies for free. I rather hoped Al would settle for him so that I could get to see free movies for the rest of my life.

But another marriage had no appeal. Since John's disappearance Al had discovered the advantages of being alone, free from the constraints of married life, able to concentrate on her painting. And she was certainly taking off. Her canvases littered the place, one of the bigger ones standing in for my bed head.

I asked her once if she minded not having had a family.

"I have one, darling. I have you."

"Didn't you fancy anyone after John left?"

"Several, darling, but after John bolted I learned the value of my own space and decided to stick with it. Love can be too demanding. Life is a whole lot simpler if left on the level of sexual desire. That's why I am worried about you. You've taken a long time to get around to it but now you've discovered sexual desire don't be blinded into thinking it's love. In any case, he's too old for you. Old enough to be your father, Lena. I see warning signs. You need someone your own age to keep you company through life, not someone who is going to die years ahead of you and leave you lonely."

"But I never needed my father; why should I need one now?"

"We all need fathers. You thought you didn't but, believe me, you were missing one."

She looked sombre for a moment.

"Your father was a louse. Why your mother adored him so I will never know. He was a womaniser, vain and a liar, and he caused her a lot of anguish. They were married far too young and perhaps under normal circumstances they might never have married, but you were on the way and they were forced into it. Values were very different then. Keeping up appearances was all that mattered. God, what a lot of emotional stress there was at that time. I can remember it. I wonder you didn't absorb it in the womb. They say babies can, you know."

Perhaps I had but what did that matter now I had found Mieciu? Love was the answer and would be for ever after.

Al shook her head. "There is no ever after but you are too young and deliriously happy to believe it."

She was not alone in her objections. Mieciu had them, too.

"How can you know what love is? How can you swear to love me for ever when you are still too young to understand how time changes people? This is infatuation and you must put me from your mind. Get on with your career. That's important. And find someone your own age to marry and have children by. I am twenty years older than you. It's too big a difference."

"So you feel nothing for me?"

"Of course I do, Silly! How could I not? You burst into my tired old autumn like a spring breeze and renew my flagging spirit. But there is danger in this for me as well as for you. What will happen when I am sixty and you are forty? You will still be in your prime and needing sex and I shall be too worn and tired to give it to you. We'd hit trouble then. You might go off with somebody else."

"How could you think of such a thing?"

"You forget I am a doctor and how much I know about life. I would understand but the hurt would be there and I don't want any more hurt. I have seen enough. Too much. Things you can never imagine. All I want now is peace and tranquillity."

His protestations were useless. I knew I would never hurt him and nothing either he or Al could say would make me deviate from my chosen path, which was to pin down and marry Mieciu.

Which I did. After seven years of dogged persistence on my part, he gave in. In that time I had travelled hundreds of miles by train and plane to be with him on holidays and weekends off, for after completing my training in Hull, I went to work as a reporter for the *Yorkshire Post* in Leeds and then in Manchester, Liverpool and Belfast for the *Daily Mail*.

In all that time I was faithful to him in spite of other approaches, but one weekend I had had enough. We quarrelled and I said a weary goodbye. "I've done my best to show you how much I love you but I see now that I have been wasting my time," I said, and walked out.

The next morning he was round at Al's place and asking me to marry him.

"I guess you'll never see sense," he said, "so I might as well try to teach you some."

We married quietly in London at the Kensington Register Office with only Tim, mother, Al and two of Mieciu's Polish friends present. We honeymooned in Paris for five days and then returned to the yellow brick detached house we had bought around the corner from my aunt. It had a central staircase and parquet floors and stood in a large walled garden with a terrace, a wide lawn and a shrubbery of ancient laurels, rhododendrons and hydrangeas, a rampaging rose bed, half a dozen apple trees, two weeping willows and three flowering cherry trees. We painted the rooms in bright colours and filled them with books and paintings, one of them a 2 x 2 metre abstract of Al's – a wedding present – that glowed in rich autumnal colours above the fireplace.

"Now I have everything," Mieciu boasted happily. "A beautiful wife and a lovely home. My first real home since leaving Warsaw. After all the loneliness suddenly so many riches... Even my own cherry trees!"

He started a wine cellar and I began collecting classical music records. He taught me to play chess and we took up fishing from the river bank on Sunday afternoons. He was confident he would catch a pike one day.

"Then I shall cook you a marvellous meal," he grinned, his eyes shining with anticipation. "Pike done the Polish way, with nutmeg and horseradish sauce."

"Forget it," I said hastily, stomach churning. "Pike eat rats."

One of his favourite composers was Chopin, although listening to his music was painful. Those ringing, intensely

30

patriotic compositions reminded him of a country he could no longer return to, of the home and parents lost in the destruction of Warsaw.

"Can we go for a short visit?"

"Too dangerous. All expatriate Poles are considered traitors by the Communist government. At the end of the war they did offer a safe return to those who had left to fight with the Allies but those who were gullible enough to believe it disappeared."

He was pensive a while, then added: "But the Communist regime won't last forever and then we can go. I shall take you to the Masurian Lakes where I used to swim in summer and skate in winter. And we'll go to the Tatra Mountains where I used to ski."

"I'd love that," I said and was filled with tenderness for him, for this stranger in a strange land who had come through the Second World War and halfway across a continent to start a new life in England and get stuck with me.

Life is full of such quirks of fate. While he was attending war wounded as an MO with Polish forces on the battlefields of France, North Africa and Italy and contracting tuberculosis (which left him with a collapsed lung) in a waterlogged dug-out medical station at Monte Cassino, I'd been at school, having mad crushes on my women teachers, spending my spare time roaming fields collecting mushrooms, picking blackberries, robbing orchards, camping in woods, earning my Girl Guide badges.

How strange that seventeen years after the war he should marry me. This grown man who had seen such terrible things… How could he love me? What could such an untutored, unsociable and rebellious creature as I give him? For, although 28 when we married, I was a child still, emotionally vulnerable, tomboyish and more at ease in the company of men, hardly aware of myself as a woman, but growing stronger and more confident all the time. Because he loved me. Because he was friend and lover and father figure rolled into one. I would have died for him. With him in my life I felt as strong as a tree, deep-rooted in good earth from which sturdy branches would grow. I was safe, self-confident. Everything would be all right from now for the rest of my life. I had no doubt about it.

And for the time we had together it was. More than all right. Wonderful! Man was a great discovery... The first one I had slept with and he was a God. A wise and generous God who opened the world to me. Patient with my youth and ignorance, he taught me about fine wines and good food, how to be a gracious hostess, how to drive; took me to dine at top restaurants, bought me expensive dresses, my first ball gown, my first watch, my first manicure set; took me to my first ballet and opera and on my first holidays abroad, to St Tropez, Nice, Menton and Monte Carlo.

I loved him effortlessly and without reserve and could hardly wait for the end of the working day when we would be home together. I was learning what a gift it is to have someone all your own, someone always on your side (even when you're wrong), whose easy nonchalance and laughing eyes can melt you at a glance. I was so proud of him and of the fact that he loved me. I never thought, not once, that anything could happen to destroy what we had. I never thought of time, of sickness, of death. The words had yet to appear in my vocabulary. I drifted in a pink cocoon of self-absorbed happiness, completely unaware of the worm at the root of everything, thinking only how splendid life was, how miraculous, and of how many children I would give Mieciu to make up for all he had lost.

What a child I was! Never thinking beyond the day.

He tried in vain to instil a note of reality into my scatty head.

"If anything happens to me I don't want a fuss. Just a simple service and the plainest headstone."

I could hardly believe what I was hearing.

"Why must you talk about dying? How can you even think of it when we are so happy?"

"Because everything can be annihilated at a stroke, darling. We are not immortal. You don't seem to realise it and I am afraid for you if something should happen to me."

Had he suspected that he would die soon? Was this a gentle warning? Seven years later and it was all over. He died from stomach cancer, a wreck of a human being after six months of suffering I wouldn't put a dog through. It was a weary, threadbare little ghoul that left me, an old, old man with winter in his face. Not my Mieciu at all. Died saying: "Try not to grieve too much."

And I was left with shards of glass in my heart and the first wounds of my life.

As long as he had been alive and fighting I had enough strength for two. The hub-cap eyes, rice paper skin, vomit, bed sores and bed pans, the daily injections I administered during his time at home were new and scary to me but did not repel. Only shredded my heart little by little.

"You're a darling," he said one day. "I never thought you could take it."

"Take what?"

"Things like vomit and bed sores and having to wipe my bottom."

"I love you. It's no problem. Together we'll lick this thing."

But that was another lesson I had to learn. You can't lick everything, no matter how determined you are; and watching his coffin being lowered into the chill soil of a sullen winter's day, I was engulfed by pain from all directions.

So this is what it's all about, I thought bitterly. And shaking my fists at the sky screamed out: "And screw you, too, God!"

Unfair on God, I know. But at that time I wasn't inclined to be reasonable.

* * *

Al said afterwards: "Come back and stay with me for a while, at least until you feel stronger. I hate to think of you brooding all alone in your place."

But I wanted to brood all alone for the house was redolent of Mieciu, his scent and the echoes of his voice in every room and this was comforting. Like every wounded animal I needed to be alone to lick my wounds and try to make sense of the horror that had befallen me. I needed to cling to his belongings and talk to him as if he were still around, needed to set a place for him at the table, brush his suits, turn the pages of his bedside book each night, sleep with my face against the pyjama jacket he'd died in. Its musky odour filled my nostrils and I inhaled it deeply in a crazy attempt to draw that last faint manifestation of his being deep into my lungs.

Al tried again, insisting that I lunched with her at weekends and coming to my house every morning to see that I was up and ready for work. Fortunately, I had decided to continue working until children came along and this was something I had to get up for, although why or how I continued to drag myself to the office when I no longer saw any purpose in existence I did not know. And I wasn't much good for anything when I got there.

"It will take time," Al said, stowing some of Mrs MacDonald's pre-cooked meals into my freezer. "In eighteen months, two years or three, it won't hurt so much."

I was outraged. "But I want it to hurt always. I don't ever want to forget."

"You will have to let him go, you know. It's what he would have wanted. He wouldn't be at all pleased if he could look down and see the state you're in now."

As if I cared what state I was in! I was numb with misery, all thought and feeling anaesthetised. Mieciu had gone. What did I care now for life, for sunlit days, starry nights, sunsets and rainbows, flowers and birdsong? My love lay deep in yellow clay, belly filled with blowflies, eyes clotted with worms. Eyes I had loved to kiss, running the tip of my tongue lightly under his lashes. He had given me shape and articulation. Without him I was floundering in a sea of emotions that were all new and terrible to me. I felt physically sick. Terrified. Threatened. Wanted out.

The day he was buried a curtain descended between the world and me and in its sombre shade I began to disintegrate. Now that I had been made aware of death I saw it skulking all around: behind hospital walls and funeral parlour curtains, in old folks' homes, on butchers' hooks and fish shop counters, in cut flowers, decaying trees and falling leaves, in rotten fruit and dust and rust and garbage rot, in foxed books, stilled hands on clocks, in discarded condoms on the street. The symbols were everywhere. Why hadn't I noticed them before and thought about the message they conveyed?

Mole-like I groped my way through the days, oscillating restlessly between murderous rage and despair, clinging crazily to the remnants of Mieciu's life. I slept in his pyjamas, wore his shirts and sweaters, used his comb and toothbrush and tore my heart over the lock of hair I'd taken from him the day he died. It was a silvery lock, soft and silky because I'd washed his hair the day before. How like a starving composer he'd looked that day! Gaunt and hollow eyed. Long hair turned white in his anguish. It was all I had left of him, the only tangible proof that he had once existed. It was as soft as the sigh that filled my heart when I kissed it.

35

Two years later it dawned on me that he would not be coming back, that his clothes would always be empty, and his chair, and the place beside me in the bed. He was no longer there for me to kiss and hold and run to and never would be again. This was no nightmare from which I would soon awake. This was screaming reality and when it hit home I felt gutted like a fish, the hole where my heart should have been filling with an icy hatred of the world and of everybody in it.

Beggars, tarts, stinking bag ladies, whey-faced druggies and rheumy-eyed alkies especially got to me. They were useless. Why were they allowed to live? I hated them. Hated them with a blind, unreasoning passion because they were still alive and Mieciu was not: a man with so much to give, much loved by his patients, much loved by me. Why did God take the best and leave such Nolde grotesques permeating the air with the reek of their unwashed bodies, their piss-stained clothes and the rot that was in their bowels?

My fury tipped over. Shocked, uprooted and too immature to deal with the existential anxiety one's first experience of death can bring, I began to hoard sleeping pills coaxed cunningly from my doctor and hid them in a top drawer of my dressing table, where Al found them one morning when she was looking for some nail scissors.

I was drinking coffee in the kitchen when she appeared in the doorway with three bottles of Nembutal in her hand and a face like a thundercloud. She didn't say anything, only slammed the bottles on the table.

My cheeks flamed. "All right, so I've been thinking about it. I don't see how I can go on living without him. Life is just too lonely. Too difficult. Too purposeless. Once it was so full of promise. Now all I ever wanted is six feet underground. It's so horrible. Horrible. How can anyone stand it?"

She sat down at the table and poured herself a coffee.

"Don't be so damned silly. You can't quit after the first setback in your life. You must bear it until it gets easier to bear and you have learned to rise above the experience. I won't have you contemplating ending your life, Lena. You don't bail out when the going gets rough. Life is tough. There will always be hurts. You will have to learn to deal with them."

"I don't have to do anything. I don't want to eat or drink or breathe again without Mieciu."

She placed her hand on my shoulder, gripping it firmly.

"Darling, get a life. You are too young to close the door. You have a chance to start all over. Take it. He would want you to involve yourself in the world again. It's a miraculous place you know, and a miracle we are here. Make the most of it. The last thing I want is to see the memories turning you into an emotional cripple. You must learn by this experience and go on. Why not get a new job in another town, another country? Anything. Anywhere. Just don't stay here moping. This is life. It's a river of pain with occasional happy landings on the banks before we get caught up again in its currents. You have to hang on in there and wait for those happy moments. And there will be more. They will come. And even though you won't believe me now there will be other loves."

"Not like him. Not ever again like him. Like it was."

"Of course not. Nothing is ever the same the second time around. How can it be? The intensity of first experience can't be repeated. But new loves will come, Lena. Believe me."

Her eyes misted with memory.

"I once felt as you do now – full of hatred for the world and not wanting to live. I lost my first love, too. No, not John. He was on the rebound, but a man who was for me as Mieciu was for you – a god. He died in an avalanche while skiing in Austria and I wished I'd died with him. I thought I would never get over it. I still haven't. Not totally. It still hurts when I think of him but

I have learned to handle the pain and am able now to block it off when it arises. You will learn to do this, too."

I hadn't known about her skier. "What was his name?"

"Tom. He was six feet tall with blond hair and blue eyes. He was a Cambridge Blue, a hurdler and he wrote short stories. He was twenty-one when he died. Unfair, don't you think?"

"I'm sorry. I didn't know."

"Why should you? I don't talk about him but I still think about him a lot."

I felt ashamed. Why was I feeling so hard done by when Al had been carrying an equal hurt around with her all these years? And, what's more, finding life worthwhile in spite of it. Just what the hell had I been thinking of in contemplating suicide? Did I honestly want to inhabit the land of the dead just yet? Mieciu had invested in me, shown me love and enhanced my sense of being. How sad if all that effort should go to waste.

"I guess I owe it to Mieciu to continue."

"You owe it to me, too."

"I'm a self-pitying fool am I not?"

"A fool and a half, my darling. What are you trying to prove with all these floods of tears? That if you weep long and hard enough you can win Mieciu back? And if you did? Would he thank you for bringing him back only to have to die all over again?

"Stop dwelling on the painful bits, Lena. Remember the good times and be grateful for them. Go forward. Find some justification other than love for living. Try to find what Camus called 'life appeal'. It isn't so difficult. There are other things that make life worthwhile: work, travel, books, music, painting… Start painting again."

I didn't take up painting but I found a purpose for going on. I decided to write a book about Mieciu, about his dying, what it meant to me, what it taught me. Above all, he would be on record as having existed and that idea pleased me enormously.

Al was thrilled. "Splendid. It should be cathartic. And then, when you have got it all off your chest perhaps you can start painting."

* * *

A few months later, after interesting the Winston Churchill Memorial Trust in the idea of my book and with enough money from them to support me financially, I set off for a faraway place where I could write in peace and get a grip on myself.

A friend had tipped me off about a place in Portugal. This was a restored Carthaginian fortress on the Atlantic coast 200 miles south of Lisbon. The owner, Count Luis de Castro e Almeida, took in a few paying guests and gave them the run of his home. I booked in for three months.

"How do you know you're not committing yourself to Count Dracula?" Al joked.

I had plenty of time to worry about that remark as the taxi from Lisbon airport took me deeper into the remoter regions of the Lower Alentejo. So just what was I doing in a faraway country where I didn't know anyone or speak the language? Suddenly I had misgivings.

It didn't help either that we arrived in the dark. Past midnight. Bumping through a sleeping village where not even a dog barked, to where the pock-marked road petered out at a small tree-lined square. Castle battlements loomed blackly against a sabled sky. Sea boomed nearby.

The taxi deposited me at a tall wrought iron gate and opening it I found myself on a short drawbridge over a dry moat from where the scent of lemon trees drifted upwards. Apprehensive, I tugged at the bell beside the heavy wooden door and waited. A rusty iron lamp creaked overhead in the wind. Shades of Jamaica Inn, I thought, and as the bell tolled for me throughout stone-flagged halls I felt like bolting. But where to? The taxi was gone. And anyway, too late. The door swung open and a plump, fresh-faced girl with shining black hair and dark eyes was smiling at me.

"I'm Lucilia," she said, taking my suitcase. "Please come in and have a seat." I will fetch Dom Luis. He is waiting for you."

I sat down on a red plush chair and looked around the entrance hall. It was spooky, dimly-lit and filled with heavy furniture. French engravings hung on dark wood-panelled walls, suits of armour gleamed in shadowy recesses, pikestaffs and crossed swords brooded over doorways. Someone's death mask lay on the table close to my elbow.

Well, this was it. I could see my future writ large. Death by pikestaff. Entombment in a suit of armour. (After I'd satisfied the count's lust, of course.) What would he look like? Never having met a real-life count before I had no idea what to expect. I imagined him sweeping in, tall, dark and wicked, wrapped in a flowing black cloak lined with scarlet silk.

Instead, Count Luis stepped out of the shadows in his pyjamas: a small, slightly-built man with salt and pepper coloured hair going thin on top and soulful brown eyes in a long lugubrious face.

He smiled and his teeth, still his own at 75, were yellow with nicotine stains and as crooked as old tombstones. He wasn't wearing anything like a black cloak with a scarlet lining but a fawn wool dressing gown with a Black Watch tartan collar and cuffs, blue and white striped winceyette pyjamas and a pair of scuffed brown leather carpet slippers. Hardly Dracula gear, I thought, and felt comforted.

"Welcome to my home," he said in a rich baritone voice and shaking my hand gave me a toothy smile. "What a pleasant surprise you are. When you wrote and said you were a widow looking for some peace and tranquillity I expected an old lady with blue-rinsed hair. Instead, you are a young auburn-haired beauty. A lovely sight for an old man's eyes."

Insisting that I had something to eat in spite of it being so late, he showed me into a panelled dining room and sent in Lucilia with onion soup, crusty bread and cheese and a jug of red wine. I ate at one end of a long refectory table lit by tall candles in silver candelabra. There were twelve red plush high-backed chairs around the table, ancestral portraits on the panelled walls and a dresser at one end of the room gleaming with three rows of sixteenth-century Spanish silver soup plates. In a stone fireplace tall enough to stand in, a last log spluttered and filled the room with the scent of eucalyptus.

After supper, Luis showed me to my room, taking me out across the courtyard with its tinkling Moorish fountain and up a steep stone staircase to the roof. He led the way across the battlements with a hurricane lamp in his hand.

"You're the lady in the tower room," he joked. "But, unlike most ladies in towers, you will be free to come and go as you please."

"I'm relieved to hear it."

The door to the tower room creaked like one in a Hammer Horror movie but I need not have worried. The room was welcoming. Not festooned with cobwebs and bats. It was large and airy with a high vaulted ceiling, whitewashed walls, a highly-polished red tile floor and a vast double bed with a hand-painted headboard and crisp white linen edged with lace. There was even an en-suite bathroom. I felt decidedly better.

"You are sharing the tower with a screech owl," Dom Luis said. "Don't be scared into thinking it's a ghost if you hear it in the night. In any case, all our ghosts here are friendly."

He stretched out a slim brown hand and patted my cheek.

"Poor child. You look so thin and exhausted. A bit like a ghost yourself. But we will soon take care of that. This place will be good for you. And our food. In a few weeks you will be blooming."

He left me then and, too tired to unpack or even shower, I undressed and fell into bed. I felt very small in it, alone and abandoned and so sorry for myself. Would this grief dog me for the rest of my days? Would there ever be any respite from it? Any day free from the endless thinking of it? Would I ever get off this treadmill? Out of this trap? My face puckered and I began to cry, deep subterranean sobs wracking my body until exhaustion overtook and I slept.

* * *

The morning sun awoke me, fingers of roseate light strobing the cool blue room through the cracks in the shutters. Seven a.m. April in Portugal. And outside the world stirring: flower heads unfolding, feathers being shaken out, spidery legs stretched, the sounds of squeaky yawns, the clearing of cockerel throats, shuffle of tiny feet, happy prattle of house martins, a dog bark, shoes scrunching on shingle, the creak of oars and the faint thud of surf.

I lingered sluggish in the soft sheets but the sounds enticed me. What sort of a place had I landed in? Rolling out of bed I slipped into my dressing gown and padded barefoot onto the terrace.

It was an effervescent morning, glistening like a Monet canvas, paint still wet: a pale, new-washed sky scumbled with flocks of cloud, a blue smudge of distant hills, dark green woods laced with light mist, a shallow brown river opening out into a placid, pewter-coloured lagoon. A man in a skiff was rowing steadily across the lagoon, a cormorant in his wake, raking the surface of the water. At the mouth of the lagoon a restless cobalt-green sea spent itself on a long sandy spit while straw-coloured dunes swelled north and south as far as I could see.

Enraptured, I let out a long, low whistle followed by a wild cry of joy. Wow! What a place! Surely it was on the edge of Heaven?

Spirits soaring, I showered hurriedly and pulled on old jeans, a sweater and sandals. There was no time to wait for breakfast. I had to be out there and a part of everything before anyone else got there first.

I raced downstairs, grabbed a couple of hot, freshly-baked rolls from a tray the village baker had just left in the hall, tugged open the heavy main door and sped wing-footed into the pristine day.

Luis said the place would be good for me and so it proved. The sun thawed the ice in my soul, softened my pain, illumined the dark corners of my heart. The wind cleared my head of its rage. I browned like a nut, put on weight, lost my haunted look, began to feel part of the world again. Wanted to. That was the achievement.

Even better, I had started to write *'All the Days of His Dying'*, the words coming effortlessly, my typewriter racing along as I sat out on my terrace unburdening my soul beneath a bright blue sky. I worked every day from 9 a.m. to lunch at 2.30 p.m. and took the rest of the day off to read and swim and roam the surrounding woods and beaches with Luis's two black Labrador dogs tagging along beside me.

It was a time of my life when my senses, heightened by grief, were alert to all the wonders nature cared to show me: moonlight dazzle on the lagoon, wind ripples on the dunes, tousled-hair clouds in cornflower-blue skies, the purple shadows cast by green leaves on ripening lemon skins, the chaste gleam of rock roses in cool, dark woods, the patterns on butterfly wings and beetle backs, on flower petals, leaves and sea shells, in bird song and bee dance, in rocks and cliff faces. All elated me in a way they had never done before. It was as if I were seeing the world for the first time, aroused from my cocoon of self-absorption and suddenly aware of the numinous in nature. Sometimes, looking into the heart of a flower or marvelling at the pattern of a butterfly's wing, I felt excited, light-headed, as if on the edge of something.

When I tried to explain this to Luis he laughed and patted my shoulder. "Are you telling me you have found God in this dusty corner of Portugal?"

"Well, not God exactly, but certainly a sense of something 'other'. Does that sound very silly?"

"Far from it," he replied. "There is a mystery to be sure but it's just not worth pondering imponderables that our brains are too small and undeveloped to comprehend. We shall never find answers until we die and probably not even then, so why waste time trying? As long as we are alive it doesn't matter why we are here or what for and when we are dead it won't matter either. Life is wondrous enough just to be going on with, isn't it?"

Yes, it was. I smiled. I knew that now. "I guess the place is getting to me or else you are feeding me hallucinatory foods."

"No," he chuckled. "It's not the food. It's the place. It's a magical place and gets to receptive people like you. You have changed, you know. You have blossomed and I like to think it entirely due to my care."

"Can I stay here for always, Luis?"

"For as long as you like if that's really what you want. You can have my farmhouse on the dunes. But would that be wise? You are far too young to be opting out now. Yes, this is a glorious, regenerative place but a place to come to at the end of your life not in the middle of it. There are dangers in solitude. One day you will ask yourself why get up so early or why go to the market today. Why not go tomorrow or the day after tomorrow? Then, why do this or that or anything at all?

Communing with nature is good for the soul to a certain extent but we grow only with other people around us who are growing as well. They give us goals and we need goals when we are young."

"But I would have goals. I would write. Paint."

"Can you write about life if you don't practise it?"

"I don't feel ready yet to go out and practise it."

"I think you have the capacity to look beyond all the pain you have experienced, my dear. You are an affirmative person. You wouldn't be writing the book if you were not. You'll build a case for going on with life, never fear. And one day a rich harvest of happiness will come your way even though you think that's impossible now."

"Thank you Gypsy Luis," I laughed. And retired to bed little knowing that another chapter of my life was about to begin.

The next morning I lay reading on the beach. It was a lion-tinted day with an ebullient sun. The sea drummed softly on the shore. Sea holly chinked in the breeze. A kestrel hung overhead, pinned on the wind.

I lay shirtless in the dunes, browning my back and reading *Anna Karenina*. I was at the point of Anna's last train journey, the disordered thoughts accumulating in her feverish mind, the fearful visions of deception, grief and evil taunting her. Poor Anna! Her state of mind was all too familiar. I'd been there. Almost done that. Recognised all too well the seductive idea of suicide.

I shivered suddenly, remembering my desolation after Mieciu died, and snapping the book shut rolled over to let the sun warm my face. What a long time ago all that anguish seemed. How relieved I was that I hadn't gone on to take the sleeping pills. How sad if I'd missed all this, I thought. For this place was balm to my fractured heart. This was as close to paradise as I would ever get.

"And how sad if I'd missed you, too," I said to the dogs who were lying watchfully beside me, tails thumping the sand.

I sat up, stretched and drank deep of the minty wind until my lungs ballooned with it. I felt soothed and clear minded. Drinking in the breeze was a simple delight. Not so long ago I'd have been indifferent to it. Like Karenina, seeing only the dark side of things, not wanting to live longer, seeing no point to life without love.

Now that dark side was fading and I was changing, acquiring a new strength that was not only physical. I was learning to accept, to adapt, and while acceptance was not without its difficulty, I knew now that the trick was to live in the present and that I would cope.

I glanced at my watch and stood up. It was almost lunchtime. And Dona Margarida, Luis's wife, always put on a good spread. If I stayed with them much longer so would I.

"Time to go, dogs!"

I pulled on my shirt, stuffed the paperback book into the pocket of my jeans and raced them to the sea.

It was there that I found the next love in my life.

* * *

He was well-built, tall, with soft brown eyes and thinning black hair that was almost silver above his ears. Sixty something. Serious type. Distinguished. He was sitting on a rock staring out to sea, watching a skein of small birds feinting at the waves, light and free and heading for the edge of the world.

He turned and smiled at my approach. Nice shy smile.

"Hello," he said. "Isn't this a marvellous day?"

46

"And a marvellous place. On the edge of heaven, don't you think?"

He smiled again and I thought how kind his eyes were. And dark. Dark as coffee beans. Mature Java. I liked his big, rather imperious nose.

"Are you staying with Luis?"

He nodded. "I've just arrived. And you?"

"Yes. I've been here quite a while now. A few weeks. I was just on my way back to lunch. It's almost time."

He stood up, brushing sand from his grey slacks.

"Good. I'm ravenous."

He fell into step beside me and we headed back around the point towards the village. The sea boomed against the shore tossing us gifts as we passed: shells and glossy stones, bright green weed, the sun-blanched branches of trees. The sky was wild, rigged with big-bellied cumulus like galleons bent on New World discoveries.

"It's like the first place in the world," he sighed, voice as soft as melted chocolate. "So spare and fresh and new."

"So beautiful it hurts. Makes me ache. Funny how beauty can do that to you. There are times when I am so overwhelmed by it I feel like weeping."

"I'm glad you can still feel that way about nature. Unfortunately, most of us get locked into city and suburban life and lose that capacity for simple delight in the rush for power and celebrity. Such artificial concepts, I think."

His name was Syth Hardy and he was from Edinburgh where he produced documentary films about Scotland.

"I've been in Lisbon advising on the development of a tourist film festival," he told me. "I thought I'd make the most of being in Portugal again and come and spend a week with Luis."

"So you have been here before?"

"My wife and I have been here a couple of times. It's one of the most soothing places I know in the world, one that lingers forever in the memory. I wanted my wife to join me this time but she suffers greatly from osteoporosis and doesn't like leaving home now."

He looked at me with a clear, steady gaze, and I thought how sweet he was. Gentle, too. A man of integrity. A bit like an elder statesman.

"And have you been here before?"

"No, this is my first visit but it won't be the last. It's a magical place. Just the spot to iron out one's soul."

"That sounds serious. Is your soul giving you problems?"

"Don't we all have problems with our souls from time to time?"

"It all depends on one's temperament. I don't worry very much about mine."

"Well, I've been having a lot of trouble. That's why I am here. To sort out the knots and decide what to do with my life."

"Ah, so you're the journalist. Luis told me he had a beautiful newspaper woman staying with him for three months."

"I think Luis has a tendency to exaggerate," I said shyly.

"I understand you're writing a book?"

"Yes. It's about my first experience of love and death. My husband's death. I want to explore its impact on me, somehow."

"It's an awfully big subject."

"I know, but I need to say something. Trying to lay the ghosts, I suppose."

He stopped suddenly, emotionally affected.

"I am so sorry. It moves me to think of someone so young going through such anguish. Isn't it difficult writing about it?"

"Sometimes I'm awash with tears but I think it's cathartic. It's helping me to come to terms with a disastrous experience. I also want to leave behind a record of his existence. Does that sound mad?"

"I'm moved," he said, adding wistfully: "Was it very good, what you had?"

"I'll never feel that way again, that's for sure. I don't see how it's possible to repeat the delirium of first love."

A small frown puckered his brow. "You were fortunate in a way. Your husband died while love was still intense."

"We had only seven years."

"There you are, you see! Your love hadn't had time to grow stale as most loves do with time. Even the greatest passions fade with the practicalities of marriage and having children, keeping the house clean, the grass cut and the bills paid."

The idea shocked me. "I can't accept that. It's a terrible thing to say. If love is diminished by reality then surely it wasn't love in the first place?"

He was laughing, but not unkindly. "I envy you your faith in love."

Luis was waiting for us at a table set for three in a cool corner of the courtyard. The dogs were already under the table, one of them providing a soft cushion for my bare feet.

Luis poured white wine into tall, green-stemmed glasses. "It's just the three of us for lunch. Four guests have left and two have gone on a day trip to the Algarve." He smiled. "I see you two have already met. I hope you like each other."

We ate tortillas and crispy green salad with onion rings followed by pineapple fritters, washed down with copious amounts of wine. The conversation was lively, punctuated with outbursts of laughter. Luis, who spoke perfect English, could be outrageous and Syth had a pawky sense of fun. I liked the sound of his voice, his quiet self-assurance, his serenity. I was surprised at how easily we were getting on and hoped the afternoon wouldn't end too soon.

Luis broke the spell. Going for his siesta. "If I don't have my nap I shall never live to be 100 which is my every intention."

He went off only to return a few moments later with a couple of straw hats.

"The sun is coming round. Don't sit in it without a hat."

I put one on, a sun-crisped straw that reminded me of Mieciu, and poured coffee. I was preoccupied, thinking of him, remembering him in his battered Panama hat bowling down to Nice in the old Porsche, the smoke of his cigar singeing the brim. How proud he had been of that hat, wearing it everywhere he could because he thought it made him look the perfect English gent. He'd worn it when swimming and, on one occasion, even while making love in the stippled shade of woods near Digne and I'd laughed so much I hadn't been able to do it.

Small arrows pierced my heart. How rich we were that day: sensuous with the heat, mouths stained purple with wine, half naked bodies burnished by the sun, and in our nostrils the heady scent of the Midi, of umbrella pines, eucalyptus and baked red earth. If I concentrated hard enough I could still recapture the warmth of his skin against mine, the moistness of it, his breath against my cheek and his heartbeats against my heart.

"Come back to me," my companion said.

"Sorry. The memories still catch me out sometimes. Just when I think I am in control."

"Don't control them too much. In the end they are all we have. Do you want to talk about it? I'm a good listener."

"I'm beginning to come to terms with my loss. Not so long ago I was devastated and enraged and didn't know how I would find the strength to go on living. I kept lashing out at God for being such a sadist in allowing us love, only to snatch it back in the cruellest ways. It's a normal reaction, I know, but I didn't want to go on living without Mieciu. I started to collect sleeping pills thinking they would be the way out."

He looked startled. "Oh no! Don't tell me you attempted to kill yourself?"

"No. Only brooded about it. Luckily my aunt found the sleeping pills and flushed them down the loo. I don't know if I'd have done it or not but the whole idea was very seductive. I was blinded by pain, unable to think straight."

"How could you even think of such a thing when you are so young and there is still so much left to see and do?"

"I didn't want to see or do anything without him."

He made as if to take my hand but restrained himself, saying quietly: "There can be someone else, you know. You must believe that. You have to give yourself time. Time will alter things."

"There can't be anybody else. Not like that. Never again like that, such an intensity of feeling. Still, you are right about time changing things. My time here has already changed me, altered my perceptions. I'm not so full of rage and self-pity now. I know I shall make it somehow. Having chosen to live I'm not going to be churlish about doing so."

I dried up. Embarrassed. *Talking too much. Probably boring the pants off him.*

I stood up. "I love talking to you but it's time for me to get back to my work. We can have a swim later, if you like."

"Yes, I would like."

"See you here then, at six."

I dropped my writing and spent the next week with him, squandering golden days along the sea shore, walking in the dunes and dog-rosed woods, swimming together in the lagoon, hunting wild oysters upriver. At night we played chess in the library and talked books and films and of the places we had been.

Luis lent us his rackety Volkswagen and we explored old towns with crumbling castles, shady squares and clamorous markets. We danced at a village wedding, wandered through fields of moon daisies where black pigs rooted, watched *Scaramouche* at the open air cinema on the football pitch – Stewart Granger in swashbuckling stunts played out against a backdrop of stars in a damson sky – went night fishing on the river with Luis, harpoons strapped to our wrists, a kerosene lamp hung over the prow of the boat drawing red mullet like flurries of snow.

Happiness again. Taking it one day at a time. Never thinking where it might lead.

* * *

On Syth's last night we dined at a sixteenth-century palace in the hills where white peacocks haunted gardens swooning with night-scented honeysuckle. Our table was beside an ornamental lake, opal green with water lilies. A full moon loitered overhead. The sky brimmed with stars.

"The forget-me-nots of the angels," he said.

"The stars?"

"Every time somebody dies here on earth they plant a star in heaven. Didn't you know that?"

No. But I liked the idea and looking up I wondered which was Mieciu's.

A waiter appeared with huge prawns on a blue porcelain dish. Later he brought artichoke soup and roast sucking pig. Tucking in, I thought how good it was to be doing things with someone again, someone who listened as if he cared. I hadn't talked so much for months. Didn't know I had so many words.

"It's like a dream," I said. "I hope I never wake."

"It's better than a dream. It's reality. A reality you once considered throwing away not so long ago."

I chilled just thinking about it. How foolish it had been to entertain thoughts of suicide. How terrible if I'd gone ahead. Look what I'd have missed! I fell silent, yielding to the moment, thinking how it didn't really matter whether there was a reason for life or not. Life itself was enough. Filled with gifts. The gift of love, starry nights, restless seas, birdsong and butterflies, blue-belled woods and rainbows, and all the sunrises and sunsets I had ever seen and still had to see.

Syth raised his glass.

"These days spent here with you have been a time of gifts for me. Thank you. Thank you for being with me. You have made me very happy. It's a long time since I had so much fun. I was a bundle of tension when I arrived. You have helped me to relax and forget my problems. More importantly, perhaps, you have made me laugh a lot and infected me with your enthusiasm for everything. It astounds me that someone who has experienced so much hurt should have come through it with their love of life so undiminished. I was depressed when I arrived, feeling that life was over. I leave refreshed and optimistic and that is entirely due to you. I would like to think I have helped you, too, in some way. And I would like you to feel you have a new friend in your life, one you can turn to if ever you are in need. You can ring or write to me at my office. I will give you my card."

He was in earnest, dark eyes holding mine, his hand reaching out across the white tablecloth to brush my fingertips.

"My wish is quite genuine," he said. "I will do my best to help you in any way I can."

His touch was brief and quickly withdrawn but it disturbed me: an emotion I did not recognise.

"Thank you. That's very kind. I won't forget this time spent with you either. I haven't done much writing but I have been happy. It's been fun."

I withdrew into myself a little, alarmed at the din in my heart, hoping he couldn't hear it. What was going on? My body seemed in total disarray, cells jumping all over. And there was a singing in my blood. A regular Hallelujah Chorus.

I fell asleep that night savouring the days we had shared and thinking how close we had become in such a short time. It was good to have found a kindred spirit. A pity to let him go. But there was nothing else for it. He was married and we lived 200 miles apart. Not very happy in his marriage though…

What was it he had said? "My wife rather resents my continuing involvement in the world when she can't get out. She would like me to retire early to look after her. But she isn't neglected. I shop, cook, iron and a home help comes in twice a week. I shall always be there for her and she knows it but there is still this resentment at my being out and about and doing things. Only natural, I suppose, when you are trapped indoors, but unreasonable to want to force me into that same straitjacket. I shall resist it as long as I possibly can."

"Wouldn't a wheelchair give her some freedom?"

"She won't have one. Too proud."

I longed to put a comforting arm around him, sorry for the trap he was in, thinking what a drag his wife seemed.

"Don't let it get to you."

"I won't. It's far too soon. There are so many things I want to do, still so much I feel I can contribute to the world."

"I'm glad to hear it." (As if it was any of my business.)

Breakfast next morning was early. Syth was due to leave for Lisbon at half past eight. I came downstairs at eight to find him already sitting at the millstone table in the courtyard and Lucilia bringing out the food. It looked good – freshly squeezed orange juice, boiled eggs, ham, bread rolls still warm from the bakery – but I had no appetite and took only black coffee, stirring in three sugars to give myself some energy because I felt decidedly off-key. A hangover, perhaps.

"A superb morning," Syth said, as I sat down.

It was. There was already some heat from the sun, the surface of the lagoon was as flat as glass, the normally turbulent sea beyond the sandbar a lightly-rumpled quilt. Four little Magritte clouds hung like lost sheep on the horizon.

"I'm sorry you're going."

"I am, too."

"Will you come back next year?"

"Perhaps. But it seems such a long time to wait."

He sighed, shook himself out of his lethargy and managed a smile.

"Sorry if I seem a bit dozy. I didn't sleep last night. How about you?"

"On and off. Mostly off. Too much to drink, I guess. My mind was racing for ages."

"What were you thinking of?"

"Of departures mostly. Yours. Mine. I suddenly realised my own is too close for comfort. I'm not sure I'm ready to go back to the rat race. I've found serenity here and am tempted to stay. Luis says I can have his farmhouse rent free for as long as I like."

"No," he said firmly. "It's not a good idea at all. Oh, I understand you well enough. It is an enchanted place, especially now on a day like today. But think ahead. Think of the isolation in winter. The Atlantic winds. The lack of stimulus. It's a perfect escape for a month or two but not for ever. Do you honestly think you could live without newspapers, bookshops, art exhibitions, concerts, cinema?"

"I haven't missed any of these things while I've been here."

"That's because you have been ill in a way and in need of a complete rest. And you had your book to occupy your mind. But you are on the mend now. Soon nature will not be enough. And once the book is finished you will need other stimuli to exercise your brain."

His large eyes were shadowed with concern. "The idea of you burying yourself here appals me. Promise me you will go home and give it a try."

"I'm not your responsibility, you know. You don't have to worry about me."

"I would be a very hard man indeed if I didn't feel concern for you. I have tried in these few days we have spent together to give you friendship, to draw you out of your solitude. Now I have to leave and I feel I haven't really done much to help."

I remained wordless, overwhelmed by the fact that this stranger wanted to help at all. Fortunately, at that moment, Luis came into the courtyard to tell us the taxi had arrived and we all went out into the square.

Putting his suitcase on the back seat, Syth turned, shook hands with Luis and then looked at me. There was a tremor in his voice.

"Thank you for being here, Marlena. You have really made my holiday."

"I'll be here next year, too, if Luis will have me," I laughed. But what was I laughing about when the sky was falling in?

And then he did something which he later said was entirely out of character. He leaned forward and kissed me on the lips. The first kiss since Mieciu died. A soft sigh escaped me. Ah, Man! How easily one forgets your sweetness.

The taxi driver was impatient, sounding his horn and gesticulating. Syth climbed into the back seat and closed the door. He waved forlornly through the rear window as the cab moved off and I saw sadness in his eyes.

"Wave back," Luis urged. "He doesn't want to leave you."

But I was rooted to the spot, with a whole symphony orchestra tuning up inside my head as I savoured the taste of Syth's lips on mine. It had been just one slight, innocent kiss and yet enough to stir my heart again. I felt a flutter of recognition, an unfolding and a burgeoning of a desire I had written off as happening only once in a lifetime. But here, suddenly, was a recall to life. I had been totally unprepared for it. And now he was going away and would never know.

At this last thought I rushed forward. He couldn't go. Not like that. Not without knowing! I began to run, chasing after the taxi, waving my arms and shouting wildly for it to stop. When it did I wrenched the rear door open and fell inside, not thinking of what I was doing or what I would say. I knew only that it wasn't meant to end like that. It was meant to start. It was a new beginning.

Later, at the airport, he looked at me wonderingly.

"You're crazy to have come so far to see me off."

"Do you mind?"

"Of course not! It's a tremendous bonus to have you with me still. But you won't be able to jump on the plane as well."

We sat holding hands until his flight was called.

"Have we lost our heads because of one little kiss?" he asked. "Was that all it took? One harmless well-intentioned little kiss? Perhaps I should have kissed you on the cheek instead."

"You weren't meant to."

"But what are we meant to do, Lena? What do we do now? Where do we go from here? I don't know how to handle it. In the taxi you said we should just give in to it but it isn't as easy as that for me. I'm married. I have someone else in my life to worry about."

"I don't intend to break up your marriage. Just to see you again. We shall find a way. Don't worry."

I had never felt more certain of anything since the day I fell for Mieciu.

His flight was called and we parted. "I'll write," he shouted as he went through the gate and I watched until he was out of sight. I felt utterly bereft. Of course he wouldn't write. Naïve of me to think he would. It had been a pleasant interlude for both of us and that was where it must end. There could be nothing more. What was I thinking of? There was far too much against it. And he'd realise that as soon as he was back in the cold, clear light of the North.

Miserably I drifted out of the airport and hailed a taxi. It would be around midnight before I got back. I hoped Luis wasn't waiting up. I didn't want to have to explain my abrupt departure.

But Luis was a wise old bird.

"You don't have to say anything," he said when I stepped through the door. "I saw it coming."

"Are you critical of me?"

"Of course not. Although there could be some problems if you do get together back in the UK. But perhaps it's just as well to take life as it presents itself and not to think too much of the future. After all, the future doesn't belong to us. There is no way we can alter what has already been decided. Don't worry. The future will solve itself. Pick a beautiful rose when it's in full bloom and never think that it will wither. One never really does think of an ending to anything that is making us happy. Only avoid hurting others as much as possible. By others you will know who I mean."

* * *

Syth's letter arrived five days later and I took it out on to the dunes to read.

"Dear Lena, Luis says people come to his place as strangers and leave as friends. How friendly is friendly? And should a friendly parting be marked only by a friendly embrace?

"I have been writing this letter in my mind ever since leaving Lisbon. You have been very much in my thoughts, waking and trying to sleep. That I kissed you and caressed you in the taxi now seems unpardonable. And yet I did not think so at the time. Did you? Was it the sun and the wine and the place? Or me? Or you and me?

"I cannot separate what I think and feel from your personal situation, recovering as you are from a traumatic experience. You are vulnerable. I wanted to help you. If I hadn't I suppose we'd have left things on the level of books and places and people. How did the help I wanted to give suddenly become something else? One kiss?

"Darling, I can't see any way which will solve anything for you. You may say there is nothing to solve. There is. You are a young and lovely woman. I am 60. We came together at a highly emotional moment in your life, when you were reliving the months of your husband's death. It should have been somebody else, younger and unmarried. It can be somebody else. You must know how attractive you are.

"When we have been so happy and left unsaid so many things that didn't need saying I am not now going to spout out a lot of ponderous words. If we can meet again and be happy and not delude each other, good. The last thing I would want to do would be to go into something with you which would only upset you further."

I pored over the letter, wanting to be with him immediately, wanting him in my arms. So what that it wouldn't last? I would go forward with arms outstretched to embrace what each new day had to offer. For a while we would have shared warmth, friendship, perhaps love. And a while was good enough. A while was better than nothing. I could meet him on that basis and be happy.

But three weeks after I had arrived home I wasn't so sure. He had written to say he could stay with me for a couple of nights on his way back from a meeting in London. "If you still wish, that is," he'd added.

Did I still wish? The sunlit certainty of Portugal was beginning to fade. The day his train was due in I paced the station platform like a restless panther. What had I done? What was I getting into? Was this really what I wanted? How could I have invited this stranger into our home, mine and Mieciu's? What the hell had I been thinking of? Back in our structured lives we would both be different from the way we had been in Portugal. It was possible we would not like each other so much. My stomach quaked.

Oh God, am I really up to all this Sturm und Drang?

Too late now though to turn and run. His train was in, disgorging its crumpled commuters with a whine of relief and he was coming towards me.

Coming for me. Eyes seeking me. Looking as anxious as I felt but so good-looking, so clean and shiny and edible, that a wave of desire rushed over me. My heart sang and suddenly I was waving and running towards him and into his arms.

"This is very *Brief Encounter*-ish," he grinned. "What would lovers do without railway stations and airports to meet in?"

All my nervousness had evaporated by the time we reached home. And he seemed at ease, examining with exclamations of pleasure the paintings and ceramics Mieciu and I had collected in our travels. He was interested in painting and said he had a small collection of Scottish Colourists.

"Maybe some day I can show them to you."

Nice of him to say that. It showed he was contemplating having me in his life for some time.

Later that afternoon we strolled by the river. Dappled shade, ducks and daisies in the grass, sunlight silvering the surface of the water. Three swans flew past in single file. A bit over the top, I thought, but laughed.

"A flypast in your honour, Syth. Courtesy of Mills and Boon."

"It's a good omen."

Before dinner he gave me a present: an amber stone set in a silver ring.

"It's beautiful but you don't have to give me things."

"But I want to. I want to mark the start of something wonderful."

He raised his glass of champagne, face flowering into a smile. "To kismet. I never quite believed until now."

"I told you I could work magic."

"You did and you have. Darling, you look radiant."

"Portugal was good for me." (It had brought him to me hadn't it?)

"Was it a great wrench leaving after all that time? I think Luis had come to look upon you as a member of the family."

"Yes, leaving him was especially hard, but I promised to go back every year until he dies. And as he intends to live to be a hundred that's quite a lot of holidays."

"And the book? Is it finished?"

"Yes, last week."

"I'm so pleased, Lena. Are you happy with it?"

I pulled a face, uncertain of what I had done. "Perhaps you would read it for me and tell me what you think?"

"I'd love to. You know that. Anything to help. You must have found it cathartic?"

"I suppose so. I must have offloaded a lot of grief and anger."

"You never did tell me how you met Mieciu."

"I was running after a bus and fell near his surgery. I gashed my knee rather badly and he patched it up, saying, 'Never run after boys or buses because there's always another one behind' and that was it. I fell in love."

"That was the beginning?"

"As cataclysmic as that. Like being hit by lightning."

"So it can happen like that. I've never really believed it. I thought it was just a ploy of film makers and novelists."

"Believe it."

"Could it be happening to us?"

"I'm trying not to think about it too deeply."

We sat out in the garden swing after dinner, sipping brandy, watching the stars. So many that night. Like moon daisies in a summer meadow.

"Did you know the stars have been sending light to us for millions of years so that when we look at them they are no longer where we are seeing them?"

"I can't quite get my mind around that," he said.

"And that our universe is expanding at the rate of two million miles a second? And that our bodies are made up of stardust?"

Why the hell was I babbling on so when all I wanted was to hold him?

"What's happening out there doesn't interest me, I'm afraid. Only what is happening here." His arm stole around my waist. "My being here with you in this lovely honeysuckled garden is all that counts."

He gave me a lingering kiss and then, voice creamy with desire, said: "Do you think we can go to bed now? I've been very restrained so far but I no longer wish to be."

* * *

I was willing enough and grateful for his arms around me but his body rhythm was different from the one I had known and I remained remote, unspent and riddled with guilt. I hadn't been able to rid myself of the idea that this was an act of betrayal.

Was Mieciu watching? What was he thinking? How hurt would he be seeing me in someone else's arms?

I tossed around feeling ashamed and thinking how stupid I had been to expect it to work with someone else when Mieciu was still engraved upon my heart. *But you don't need me now, my love. There is nothing we can do now for each other. So let me be. Let me try again. Of course it's not the same but I need someone. I need more certainty than just your photograph and a lock of your hair to kiss. So look away, my darling. Look away.*

But even if Mieciu wasn't aware of my betrayal, I was. And my mind raced, bedevilled by memories of lovings long since gone: lovings here in this same bed, the last time with Mieciu on the morning he was due in hospital for his operation. He had awakened me in the pale light of dawn, wanting me in spite of the cancer gnawing at his gut, in spite of his weakness and his pain, and together we soared to the edge of time. I couldn't recall ever having given myself as fully as that before, or so tenderly, or having been so overwhelmed with rapture. Was it because behind it all were intimations of his mortality?

I awoke next morning still with a sense of unease, still unable to shake off the feeling of adulterousness and looking at Syth, whose back was turned to me, I hoped against hope that it would be Mieciu when he turned over.

But it was Syth who turned to me.

"You are spying on me. Counting my wrinkles."

"I haven't had enough time to count them all."

I tweaked his nose. "Are you staying for breakfast?"

His eyes were languorous. "If I may."

"Of course you may… In a second or two…"

He was watching me closely. "What are you up to?"

"Just looking."

"Am I so fascinating?"

"Luscious," I teased, my interest reawakening. "I shall eat you for breakfast. A little bit of this… A lick of that…"

"There are three of us now in this bed."

"I know. Shall we do something about it?"

I didn't wait for an answer. Straddled his thighs. Shouted as his penis hit my cervix.

"Oh God, am I hurting you?"

"Yes. A bit. But I like it."

His eyes, large and luminous, watched my rising passion. And this time nothing was going to stop it. I was coming away, coming free, and his face became a pale blur as the fireworks began. And after three years what fireworks! Coming away at last. Coming several times in quick succession, in crimson wave after wave, and it was as if I would faint. And then he opened in me, too, and all the pain and isolation was blotted out and I was released at last.

Afterwards, there was an awed hush over the room, a long soundlessness, and when eventually I opened my eyes I saw him smiling at me.

"That was phenomenal."

I nodded, too winded to speak but feeling suffused with radiance. It had been great having a man inside me again, being conscious of his heat, of the little flutterings at the stem of him. I'd missed it.

And then the sobbing began: a dry rasping that wracked the length of my body and seemed to come from the depths of my being. Sobs of deliverance? I couldn't be sure. But I went on sobbing for a long time until the tears began to flow and washed away the loneliness.

And so the heartache and the grief were finally suspended and the shoots of hope sprung from the frigid soil. What was there to say about that morning? That I had made a re-entry into life, a commitment to the future. A memorable couple of days indeed. Enough to keep me going until we met again.

Memorable days for him, too. "I feel stunned by it all," he said as we waited for his train to Edinburgh. He was holding my hand tightly. "It's as if you have taken possession of me. I can't stop thinking about you and it's frightening. In the beginning I thought I could keep the part of my life that belongs to you apart from my work and family but it doesn't work like that. And I am not sorry."

Clearing his throat nervously he said he was amazed at himself, at the strength of his reaction.

"Never before like this, Lena. Never before in my life. Here I am at 60 having found love. What a great gift you have given me. Even if it ended right now I would always be grateful."

His letter arrived three days later:

"Darling, those days with you are left in my mind with a kind of bloom on them, the mark you may remember Barrie once said, of a woman in love. They were days I shall never forget. They were all I expected them to be and something more. The something more is difficult to define. An absence of strain. A presence of pleasure. A coming together at last that seemed natural. I was happy with you, you gave me real happiness. I hope you were happy with me.

"That I am frightened by the intensity of feeling now around us, I admit. How shall we ever climb out again? You say that you don't look for anything more, given my position, than we have. My concern is that this may harm you, might delay the return to the involvement with life for which you say you now feel prepared. Does this make sense to you?

"Darling, how good you are to me and for me. Thank you for all the kindness, the thoughtfulness and the understanding. I keep thinking of you alone in the house with all the memories it must hold for you. My stay could have been disastrous. I am so glad it wasn't. I was happy to be with you, happier than I can very well say. So much so that I'll never forget and won't want to."

The letter moved me much more than I expected. Was this love again in my life? Something close to it, perhaps. Nothing as wild and as passionate as the first time around but almost as good and who was I to complain? I was loved again. I'd got lucky.

"The question of luck is debatable," Al sniffed, having called round to be introduced. "All right, so he is a very charming man, cultivated and kind. I can understand what you see in him but he is another damned father figure, Lena. And even older than the last one. All I can hope is that it doesn't last long."

It was to last until he died twenty-three years later.

* * *

At first we saw each other once a month by devious means. It helped that he was often on business in London and could break his journey to spend time with me. Sometimes I would join him on the Edinburgh-London train, catching it at York, and we spent a few days in the city visiting art exhibitions, the cinema, going to concerts at the Festival Hall, eating out at small Soho restaurants. Other times I took the train north for a day, taking a cheap day return to Dunbar where he would meet me in his Rover and whisk me off through Borders country to look at castles and country houses or to picnic in the Dunbar dunes.

They were unforgettable days. Days outside reality spent idling along the sea shore, wandering through rhododendron woods, paddling in brown trout streams, roaming National Trust gardens. I say 'outside reality' deliberately because the reality, the return home to an empty house, was bleak and although I had Al to run to I longed for a man all of my own again. Why had I to fall for someone else's? In between our meetings I ate my heart out but his daily telephone calls and weekly letters kept me sane.

It was good being with him. He had a calming influence on me and I felt secure in his friendship. We had long talks about books, painting, films, politics. Words I didn't know I had cascaded from my lips. Somehow they had all been buried under my grief. Now the floodgates had opened. And he listened, his head on one side, a kind smile on his lips, sometimes holding my hands in his.

I used to tease him a bit, trying to make him laugh, happy when I succeeded because he was a little too serious, worn down some days by his home situation. Not that he said much about it except to admit once that his marriage had been over long before he had met me. By that I assumed he meant the sexual part and that delighted me. He was all mine.

It seemed that his wife did little more than chain smoke, read thrillers and nag him about early retirement and he was getting sick of it.

"But I'm not the only one. There are lots of men in a similar situation," he said. "Life traps us all in the end."

"Isn't there anything creative she can do? Embroidery? Painting? How about buying her a set of watercolours?"

"She is in too much pain to take an interest in anything. She is really very dependent on me you know. I could never do anything to hurt her. She isn't strong like you."

Oh well, that was telling me. But I didn't mind too much. He was a kindly, loyal man. Of the generation that married for better or worse. (Or 'butter and wurst', as Mieciu used to joke.) Besides, I didn't want to hurt the woman either. I didn't know her. Only wanted his love and had that.

"You have refreshed me in a way I can't explain," he said one day. "I feel reinvigorated, my interest in things has been renewed. I was beginning to give up just before we met, feeling that life was over. Now I know that it isn't. Because of you I feel only halfway through."

Well, he had rekindled my life, too: stirred the senses again, made me feel human again, that I belonged and was no longer on the outside looking in. In mattering to him I had become better balanced, less introspective, no longer so entirely consumed by the treadmill of grief, ready to come out of the shell into which that grief had thrown me.

The relationship was of positive value to us both. Even if it ended soon its value would never be diminished.

But the fact that he might be holding up my return to life terrified him.

"I wonder if I am really good for you. I'll never leave you but I have no future to offer you and you mustn't let your feelings for me spoil your chances with someone else."

We were lying in the heather of a North Yorkshire moor. Sea not far away. Wind salt-rimmed. Afternoon hot and tawny. Air riffled with butterflies. A skylark was singing overhead. Such a resounding symphony from such a miniscule pair of lungs! I wondered how he did it.

"You're not listening to me."

"Yes I am. I know the score and have no regrets. But you. What about you? Don't you sometimes regret the emotional complications I have brought into your life? The guilt at all the white lies you have to tell to get away to be with me? If you don't feel half the happiness I do when we are together then the price is too high for you."

God knows what I would have done had he said yes, but fortunately I wasn't put to the test.

"We won't use scales. I think they must be about even. I have never before experienced what I have with you. In one sense I have never had the opportunity because I am not a promiscuous man. This is my first extramarital affair. Odd as that may sound these days but then I am almost an obsolete generation. But I don't mean just that. You have stimulated and refreshed me in a way I didn't think was possible.

"But you ought not to be involved with someone like me, Lena. This is the central dilemma. Is it really enough for you to snatch a little happiness with me now and then when with someone else you could have it all the time? And when something happens which may end it, won't you hate me for not insisting that this is no way out for you?"

I felt a touch of impatience. How could I answer that when no-one else had come along? We would meet that hurdle when we came to it. In the meantime I was quite content living for the day. Things would work out.

"Don't depress me. Not today. Today is too lovely for serious talk."

He sighed: "I'm just not worth ruining your life for in any sense. That's all I'm trying to say. Okay. Okay. I'm sorry. I'll stop this philosophising. Give me a kiss like a good girl."

"I'd rather kiss you like a naughty one."

***

Eighteen months later my book was published: one of the women's magazines serialised it; the *Yorkshire Gazette* did a profile, I signed books in a city centre bookstore.

"I'm having a brief taste of celebrity," I laughed when Syth telephoned with congratulations.

"Do you like it?"

"Not much. It's a bit of an ordeal but I'll live."

"What's the best thing about it?"

"Readers' letters. I'm getting a lot of them. Some of them make me weep because they are from people in the abyss I've just climbed out of and I don't know how to reply to help them."

"It must be satisfying to have strangers so moved by something you have written that they want to make contact with you."

"It is. It makes me feel that I have made a small contribution to the world. However, I know it's a mere drop of rain in the ocean so I'm not likely to get bigheaded over it."

"Don't knock it," he replied. "Even a drop of rain makes a ripple. One day somebody reading your book may be affected by that ripple, changed by it, and that will be your contribution to the sum total of things. That should make you feel good."

Al sobbed over the book until she gave herself a migraine. Weeping as much for herself as for me, she said. Thinking of her first love entombed in snow.

"All the old pain hit me again. Just when I thought I'd buried it. Just goes to show… It's always with you, surfacing when you least expect it."

"I'm sorry if I've opened old wounds for you."

"No need to be sorry, darling. That's life. And I do feel a whole lot better for having had that cry. It means I'm not entirely dried up. I hope you feel easier, too, now you have written all that angst out of you. I hope only that it isn't going to happen all over again with Syth."

"Oh, he's full of vigour. He'll live a long time… well into his nineties!"

"Dear God. I hope not. For your sake."

Syth and I met in London to celebrate the publication, putting on the Ritz and dining at the Ivy. At dinner he said: "Sometimes what is happening to us seems so strange. A little unreal. But it isn't. It has happened and is happening. There are times when I have the feeling I'm on the outside looking in and that there are forces which seem to be shaping our lives. You call them guardian angels. Well, they are strong enough."

Six months later our guardian angels did it again. Syth was invited to be a member of the jury in the first international festival of tourist films to be held in Lisbon: the one he'd been advising on the year we met. A fifth jury member was required.

"And I've suggested you," he phoned to say, giggling slightly. "After all, you are reviewing films for your paper and are a famous author besides."

"And?" I could hardly breathe for excitement.

He burst out laughing. "They agreed. All expenses paid. Now all you have to do is get a week off work."

I'd get it all right. Even if I had to give notice. But I didn't have to go that far. I had a week's holiday due.

That was how, the first week in May, we came to be touching down at Lisbon airport and spinning in a taxi towards the city's Mundial hotel: separate rooms with a connecting door which an understanding maid was easily bribed to leave open.

"Pinch me," I said, throwing open the French window to the terrace and going outside. "Pinch me really hard to see if I am awake."

He did. And, oh glory be, I was. How full of little miracles life can be.

"Tomorrow I shall light a candle in the cathedral."

"I didn't know you were religious, Lena!"

He slipped an arm around my waist and kissed my cheek. "I'm glad I can make you happy sometimes."

"Are we wrong to be so happy in a world where there is so much sadness?"

"But there is so much in the world that is right. Shouldn't we be glad about that? And while we can? For our turn for anguish will come sooner or later."

* * *

The films we had to judge were half-hour depictions of holiday attractions in various parts of Europe, including one from Scotland on the Hebrides. I made a mental note to mark that one up to please Syth. We viewed in the mornings and retired for lunch and discussions to a noisy fish restaurant on Rossio Square. Lobsters as big as cats. Vast plates of crayfish.

Evenings we dodged the other critics and dined at backstreet tabernas slung with pots of geraniums and petunias and echoing with the music of guitar and mandolin. We ate steak and barbecued pork, drank copious amounts of purple wine and drifted back to our hotel to make tender love. We made love every night. Woke mornings with bruised eyes.

"It's all the shellfish we're eating," Syth joked, pleased with himself.

There was a huge banquet at the town hall on our last night and a presentation of awards. We drank a lot and returned unsteadily to our hotel through warm streets scented with orange blossom.

"I feel so happy I can hardly breathe," he said as we climbed the hotel steps.

"Will there be anything as good as this again?"

"It isn't over yet, you know. We have tomorrow and most of Sunday. What would you like to do? Make a wish and I shall make it come true."

"I'd love to see Luis again."

"Would we have time? We need to be at the airport on Sunday by 6 p.m."

"Easy. It's two hours by taxi. We could leave early, be there by noon, come back after Sunday lunch."

"Why do I never have ideas like that? It would be marvellous. What a surprise for Luis."

"Agreed then?"

"No problem. We'll give Luis a ring when we get upstairs and tell him to kill a sucking pig."

But all dreams end half-finished. There was a message for him at the reception desk. It was from his daughter asking him to ring her.

"Oh God!" he exclaimed, face turning pale. And in that moment I was separated from him, no longer in the forefront of his mind, and felt abandoned and afraid. Was this the beginning of the end? Was our ivory tower breached? I remained silent and bowed down with anxiety.

"I must ring right away," he said and I caught the flutter of fear in his eyes.

"Of course. I will wait for you upstairs. Don't panic. It may be nothing serious."

I waited for him in a darkened room, sitting by an open window and watching people strolling in the street. Their laughter floated up to me and thinking how only a few moments before Syth and I had been doing the same, I felt weighed down by a thick blanket of despair. Had we been found out? But how was that possible? Perhaps his wife had been in an accident? Was badly hurt? Dying perhaps?

I felt sick at the thought. Didn't think I could handle that.

He arrived and turned on the light. His face was shocked and he sank down on the bed with a huge sigh. I rushed over and put my arms around him.

"My wife has fallen downstairs and broken a hip."

The bitch, I thought furiously. She's done it on purpose! And was immediately ashamed of my unreasonableness.

"It happened last night. Around midnight. She was going to the bathroom."

While we were in each other's arms, I thought and felt really shitty. I was a cheat, just like my father.

"Luckily my daughter was staying and got her into hospital. I have asked reception to see if there is a flight out early tomorrow morning." He took my hand in his. "I hope you don't mind."

Mind? Do I mind? Of course I do. I mind like hell!

"Of course I don't mind, silly! It can't be helped."

"You could stay on… Go and see Luis…"

"How could I? Without you?"

I held him close that night, held him until he slept and darkness waned and dawn appeared, pale and shivering, at the window. It will be all right, I reassured myself. Broken hips mend. The world hasn't come to an end. Only the holiday and we knew that would happen.

But my sangfroid was only skin deep and I lay awake all night, silent and torn apart, my anxiety hanging uneasily on the air, almost palpable.

Back at home, mangled by fear, I waited for his phone calls. He rang every day to tell me of his love and to report on his wife's progress. He was all right. He was coping. But after three weeks of hospital visiting he was beginning to sound tired and fretful. His wife wasn't making much headway.

I felt threatened and despairing for how could I nourish him when I was so far away? I chafed at my uselessness and then I received this letter:

"Thank you being in my life, my darling. I am never happier than when I am with you. I love you very much. You have moved into my life so commandingly that I sometimes wonder how aimless it would have been without you. I have gained so much from your love, so much confidence, that I sometimes feel overwhelmed. You are very dear to me.

"I have been reading a book by André Maurois called The Art of Living, *which I have been subconsciously applying to us. Here are two or three sentences:*

'It is a great joy to admire someone without reserve: love which is founded upon admiration of the mind as well as the body of the chosen person undoubtedly affords the keenest delight.

'The marvellous feasts of passion which fall to the lot of lovers resemble summer days when the warmth of the sun fills us with blissful languor, when the sky is so clear that we cannot imagine it tarnished by clouds, and when the humblest village of the plain becomes a mirage of magical beauty in the golden light. Days like that, with their enchanted memories and the hope they bring of others to come, provide us with the necessary strength and courage to endure the dark months of storm.

'Of what is love made which is born of desire and outlives it? Of confidence, habit and admiration. Almost all of our fellow beings deceive us, but a few of us have known the joy of meeting a woman or a man whose sincerity and frankness were genuine, who in almost every situation has behaved according to our wishes, and who in our most difficult moments has not forsaken us. Those few are familiar with that marvellous feeling: confidence. Confidence is such a precious thing that, like physical desire, it lends charms to the most insignificant of acts.'

"Perhaps it is indolent of me to borrow someone else's phrases. The accident of reading the book in your absence and the fact that he expresses so many of the feelings I have are the reason. Marlena, I love you deeply."

The letter prompted me into action. It was time to get moving again, to be more positive, to make changes. Mieciu was beyond me now no matter how much I wished him back. I had to break free from the house and the memories that while comforting and safe were making a prisoner of me. Syth's sweet vulnerability drew me. I wanted to help. I decided to go to Edinburgh to see what I could do.

He was thoroughly depressed when I arrived. His wife's osteoporosis was hindering her recovery. She needed a hip operation and he saw his life closing in.

"What I dread most is being limited more by my home situation and not having any more excuses for being out of town. How shall I see you then?" He looked at me despairingly. "The thought of being without you leaves a hole in my heart."

That was when I had my flash of inspiration.

"We are not going to let this go on," I said firmly. "I understand that you have responsibilities here and are tied by them but I am free. I shall come to you."

So I went job hunting the next day and landed work as a sub editor with *The Scotsman*. A week later I was the owner of a sunny flat at the top of a handsome Victorian tenement with a clear view of the Braid and Pentland Hills and only ten minutes' walk away from where Syth lived. Suddenly I was alive again with plans, purpose, future. The guardian angels had pulled out all the stops this time. Before long I had said goodbye to my family, to mother preparing to retire to Spain, to Tim, teacher-training in Durham, to Al, devastated to see me go but happy I had made a move.

"I'm not sure it's in the right direction," she said, "but at least it's a move away from the past."

So off I went, eager for a new start and heading towards a time of great contentment and creativity and, eventually, the happiest years of my life.

I've found a new life, Mieciu. Can you see me down here? Are you happy for me? I don't know where it will take me but I have to let you go now. Be glad for me that I am loved again.

And my new life began quite literally with a bang, the one o'clock gun going off on the Castle Esplanade as Syth and I emerged from Waverley Station.

Mills and Boon again.

"Are we living in a novel?" he asked with a huge banana grin.

"Yes. And one day I shall write it."

And so another stage of life began for me: a time when happiness prevailed. How could it not when we were sure of seeing each other several times a week, lunching at the Arts

Club, visiting art galleries, sometimes snatching a night at the cinema, a day out in the country. It was comforting to know he was living just along the road from me, sleeping with his head towards mine and able to drop in whenever he was passing.

"I think of you all the time," he said. "All the time. You have no idea how happy you have made me."

It was surprising how much we had in common – a love of books, art, travel, movies. We never could resist a book shop, Jenner's sale, a pick-your-own strawberry field, or the shortbread with afternoon tea at the Caledonian Hotel. Safe again in someone's love, thrilled with my job, I felt settled at last, no longer solitary. I was in from the cold... a new woman.

"And I feel like a new man."

"Oh, I've unbuttoned a few Presbyterian buttons, that's all."

"No, my sweet. Much more than that. You have opened the dusty cupboards of my mind, shattered the routine expectations of my life, inspired me to new adventures, cajoled me out of all my apprehensions and rigidities. You have made me feel even with the passing years that I am far from old and never will be."

Well, what can one do better than that for someone? I shared in his joy at what we had brought to life. Him for me and me for him. We were richly blessed with a fulfilling relationship despite its limitations.

"You have given my life a new meaning without which it would have withered away," he said and my heart was full.

His wife came home from hospital a semi-invalid, confined to a ground floor room and spending most of her time in bed, reading, smoking and watching television. Reluctantly, she agreed to go into a nursing home for two weeks every year while he had a break and we made the most of it.

Over the years we delved into tombs in the Valley of the Kings, swam up the path of the moon in warm sea off Korcula, listened to opera in Verona, sipped brandy under the stars of

Crete, watched belly dancers in Marrakech, had our portraits painted in Paris in the Place du Théatre.

Our portion of happiness was very large. Much more than we had the right to expect. Sometimes I wondered how long it would last and how it would all end. What was it Luis had said all those years ago? "Pluck a rose when it's in full bloom and never think that it will wither." Well, I had plucked the rose and wasn't going to worry about what might happen next.

It was also a time of accomplishment for both of us. Syth produced a book on the documentary film movement and another on the role of Scotland in cinema. I was promoted to subbing the arts and parliamentary pages and was contributing a column on travel books. During the day I studied for a BA Honours degree with the Open University. I loved my job and my colleagues were fun to work with, always good for a laugh or a joke – this was before computer technology took the soul out of us. Most of the laughter was prompted by the wicked wit of our chief copy taster, Jim Ritchie, who was soon to become my last and best of loves.

Syth's books were published in America and led to an invitation when he was 76 to do a university lecture tour. His wife and daughter said this would be too strenuous, too risky. He was too old. There would be too much stress. But he was desperate to go.

"Of course you must go," I said. "You must live all you can. Up to the very last minute."

He went and it was a great success. From the States he wrote: *"Life is full to overflowing and it's all thanks to you. You have given me the stimulus to do more than I think I would have done at my advanced age. The trip is wonderful. My hosts are very kind and take care of me. The lectures, believe it or not, are packed and I am feeling extremely vigorous and creative. The only disappointment is that you are not here beside me.*

"We have known so many joys together that I shiver when I think it might end, that one day I might lose you. I never stop thinking about you, even at this distance. I love you so. If I lose you I shall just give up and die.

"Without you I would by now have joined the aged and infirm. There used to be an annual appeal from the pulpit of our local church on behalf of the Aged and Infirm Ministers' Fund and I could picture a lot of old dodderers in wheelchairs sitting in some enclosed garden reading the Bible or the Church of Scotland magazine. To think I used to contribute film notes to that! My darling, my darling, my darling! I owe you so much.

"I admit to moods sometimes in which I feel depressed by the hopelessness of our situation. I cannot love you more than I do and as time passes the feeling grows ever stronger. I don't know what more I can do to help you other than to say you have all my love and devotion for as long as you want to have them. It may not always be enough. If you can find happiness and protection with anyone else I shall accept it, not only because I would have no alternative anyway but because I would know you were being cared for. That is more important than any feeling I would have."

I stowed the letter away with all the others he had written over the years: tender, loving, wistful letters that I'd tied up with red ribbon; letters posted from just around the corner to say he was missing me, love notes he'd hidden in the books he gave me, postcards from trips abroad that he hadn't been able to share with me. My leaving him was the least of his worries, I thought. No-one else had ever crossed my line of vision and seemed unlikely to do so. In any case, I felt I owed him and would be with him to the end. I had no doubt my supply of love for him was inexhaustible.

* * *

That time would overtake us was something I had never thought about, preferring to live only for the day. But gradually the dues were coming in, imperceptibly at first and then abruptly. One day it's Indian summer. The next it's autumn with a chill wind stirring our arthritis and reminding us we are growing old and that those we love are growing old, too. The moment came when I looked at Syth and saw that this had happened to him.

One day I saw him on the street before he saw me and suddenly I felt suffocated. He was an old man: a shaky, thin-haired old man walking tremulously across the road in a coat that had become far too long for him because he was shrinking into his bones. He was beginning to stoop, too. And there were grooves of weariness at the corners of his mouth. Marionette lines. Oh God, how unutterably weary he looked. I felt as if someone had struck me a heavy blow across the face and I was flooded with dismay. How could this dearest of men have got so fragile all of a sudden? How come I'd only just noticed?

I stood watching him and was filled with indignation at his decline. To what end this disintegration of sweetness, this noble heart and shining intelligence? Why does God wish to humble us so?

From where I was standing life suddenly looked set for disaster and filled with fear for Syth I began to run, wanting to wrap him safely in my arms. As if I could save him somehow.

He caught sight of me and put on a broad smile, pulled back his shoulders and quickened his step. Too late! I had seen the way it was going to be, that the bubble would soon burst.

"Darling!" he greeted me happily and gave me an ardent kiss. But I was close to tears and avoided his eyes, not wanting him to see the shock and pity in mine.

"You are three minutes late," I joked, slipping an arm in his. "I am always afraid when you are late that you are not coming, that you have found another woman."

He was not at his best that day. His wife was playing up again. Draining him, her clingy dependency beginning to suffocate him.

"I do my best but it's never right," he faltered.

I experienced a sense of déjà vu. So why the hell stay with the damned woman when life was so short? Why not put her into a nursing home and live while he had the chance?

"Save yourself," I blurted out. "Come to me."

But what would I have done had he taken my advice? I'd said it out of the kindness of my heart but did I honestly want to lumber myself with an old man? One who really was now looking like my father? I struggled against the mean thought, hating myself for it. But it stayed with me.

"How could I leave her when she is so dependent upon me? She would never get over it."

So what, I thought, and shrugged. "Instead you choose to throw away your chance of happiness with me. You have always done that."

A cruel, snippy, thing to say and the first time I had ever been mean to him but suddenly I was weary of it all, wanting to be free. The whole thing was too much responsibility and was beginning to weigh on me.

He reached for my hand and kissed it. And his humbleness irritated me.

"Perhaps one day we shall be together. If anything happens to my wife will you marry me?"

I was unable to look him in the eyes. Had I ever wanted to marry Syth? I had never given it a thought. In any case, it was all too late. Couldn't he see that?

"Of course," I lied, not wanting to hurt him.

He smiled, reassured by the lie. What else could I have said? He couldn't help growing old but I felt irked and irritable that he couldn't see for himself how pointless marriage would be and then I was ashamed of myself. This man loved me and needed me and I would see him through. How could I hurt him? The fetters that were beginning to oppress me were self-imposed. I had set the tender trap myself all those years ago and could see no way out of it without destroying him and I loved him too much to want to do that.

Added to this conflict that was now beginning to gnaw at me was the pain of seeing him physically diminishing. Watching him succumb to the tyranny of old age was as tough for me as it had been watching Mieciu succumb to cancer. My tenderness for Syth overflowed. I vowed I would be there for him always. Of course I would. What else was there to do? Where else to go? I would have freedom if I made a break for it but was there any value in freedom without someone to love?

And anyway, I owed him didn't I? Owed him for all the serene years he had given me; for his encouragement and love; for being there whenever I needed him; for all the joyous moments we'd shared; for all the roses and wine and perfume and books that had lined my way; for the way he had warmed my life, defrosted my sadness, eased my isolation; for the calm acceptance of my middle years. I owed him for his loyalty and devotion and now that he was stumbling towards the dark limits of his life, I would not abandon him.

But keeping a cheerful face for him was not always easy. His troubles were mounting and each new intimation of his mortality distressed me deeply. He was breathless at night, unable to sleep. His fingers were beginning to ache and curl with arthritis. A touch of gout in his big toe made walking painful. Sometimes, seeing how weary he was, my heartache was overwhelming.

I began to take extra care of him, watching his every step, taking his arm on flights of stairs, keeping my eyes peeled for people who might jostle him in the street, for muggers who might knock him over. I made him promise never to go alone to Jenner's sale and never, ever to be out late by himself.

He protested, laughing: "Oh dear, am I so very old?"

"Not very. Just a little."

"I don't feel old."

"One never does. That's what makes it all so difficult to bear. We are still thirty-year olds under our wrinkly skins."

"You will never be wrinkly, my darling."

He had never been ill in his life and resented any minor affliction like his gout and a slight deafness in his left ear. His arthritic fingers angered him and he was impatient of his need to sleep in the afternoons. He didn't appear to notice how thin his hair was becoming, how white, how more pronounced his stoop, how much slower his walk, how much deeper the pouches under his eyes, how much looser the skin around his neck. I noticed though. Noticed it all. And felt my heart tear a little every time I looked at him.

* * *

When he was 78 he had a stroke. A nurse rang me at the office to say he was in hospital and had asked to see me. I dropped everything and grabbed a taxi to the Royal Infirmary. I was on tenterhooks all the way, thinking, "This is it. This is how it's going to end."

He was in a corner of the ward, a wan, wilted little figure, wired up to a heart monitor. His eyes shone when I appeared.

"My lovely darling."

"What are you doing to me? How can you frighten me like this?"

"I'm sorry to have scared you. Don't worry. I'm going to be all right although I couldn't say a word for seven or eight hours. The doctors kept asking me questions and I could understand them but couldn't answer. It was exasperating. Frightening, too. I wanted you near me. Desperately."

His voice broke a little and sitting on the edge of the bed I caressed his face, thinking how haggard it was... how small it had become. And his hands... the skin on them like tissue paper. I kissed them gently, over and over.

"I blame myself. I shouldn't have encouraged you to do the American tour or write that last book. It was all too much for you. You got over-tired."

"Hush, darling, I wanted to do those things. They were good for me. They have greatly enriched my life and I wouldn't have done any of them if it hadn't been for your prompting. You can't blame yourself for events impossible to anticipate."

He was fortunate that it was a mild stroke. He was home again in two weeks and gradually we gathered our lives together again. His wife and daughter wanted him to rest, do nothing. But while he gave up his committees, he continued to review books and write articles on film for Scottish newspapers and to give time to helping organise a university film archive.

"I have to keep my lines open to the outside world," he said. "Not just for the sake of my sanity but because the outside world means you and opportunities of seeing you. If I could no longer be with you I'd just give up. I'd turn my face to the wall and fade away like an old Indian."

Six months later he was feeling fine and had as much energy as ever. He went off to Germany to present John Grierson's film *Drifters* to an orchestra accompaniment and a wildly enthusiastic audience. On his return he started oil painting lessons with me on Saturday mornings at the College of Art. We planned a week's holiday in Andalucia.

Life seemed on an even keel again. He was optimistic he would make it to 90. He even felt like making love again but I took my chance to wriggle out of something I'd been finding difficult for some time because my hormones were being disrupted by someone else.

"It isn't fair to ask me. It's just too much responsibility for me, don't you see? You might have another stroke and how would I feel if you dropped dead on top of me? How would I get you back into your clothes, down the stairs and into your car?"

He giggled. "You'd have to call the police."

"And then your wife and daughter would find out about us."

"I'd be past caring."

"But I wouldn't."

"But if I can no longer satisfy you, Lena, I may lose you." That familiar male anxiety.

"That's the least of your worries, my sweet. What I feel for you goes much deeper than sex. Love outlives desire. Isn't that what Maurois said? Well, it's true."

He looked doubtful and I gave him a hug, telling him not to worry. "The skies might not be as cloudless as they used to be or the moon within such easy reach but there are still good times to come, I promise."

* * *

The main reason I no longer wished to have sex with Syth was because by this time Jim Ritchie was in my life. He and I had spent five jokey years working side by side in *The Scotsman* editorial department before realising we were soulmates. It was some time before I got to know him well because he never came out to the pub with the rest of us at breaktime and always went straight home at midnight at the end of his shift.

He was a lean, graceful man, light on his feet, with flyaway black hair and a handsome craggy face with a Duke of Wellington nose and a long, sexy mouth that turned up at the corners. His job as chief copy taster was a highly responsible one. He had to sort out and read all the copy that came in to the paper, measure it up and farm it out to relevant desks. Whenever he was on duty there was a lot of laughter from the back bench where all the senior sub editors sat. He was mischievous, quick witted, ironic, observant, a great caricaturist, and a lover of opera.

He hadn't always wanted to be journalist He'd wanted to be an opera singer for he was blessed with a fine tenor voice, but his parents hadn't been able to afford to send him to London's Royal College of Music. So Jim had settled for journalism and amateur operatics, getting all the romantic parts because he not only had the voice but was dishy to look at, too. His big chance did come with an offer of a place in the Glyndebourne chorus, but by that time he had married and had a small daughter and a wife who didn't want to leave Edinburgh.

I had always assumed Jim didn't like me because while other guys in the office shook my hand and kissed me every New Year, Jim only shook my hand. It took him five years to make up his mind to kiss me as well and when he did I was knocked sideways. It was a kiss so tender and wistful and tasting so sweet that it went straight to my heart and I stopped breathing. I couldn't get the taste of it out of my head and for weeks I schemed Mata Hari-like how to get another to confirm what I was beginning to suspect. That he was made for me.

The next kiss wasn't long in coming. I caught him alone in the sports editor's room one night, pulled him to me and started kissing him like mad.

"I'll give you twenty-four hours to stop doing that," he said.

Well, we got more than twenty-four hours. We got sixteen years of doing that and a lot more besides, having an affair for five years before it dawned on me that we could live together.

He broke down one day shortly before his retirement.

"I can't bear the thought of spending the rest of my life with my wife," he said, his voice all choked up. "Retirement with her will be unbearable. I knew almost from the start that my marriage had been a big mistake. She has made me wretched for most of our 39 years together and now I have had enough. I am leaving her and I want you to come with me."

He had never spoken of his unhappiness before and I was dismayed. For a few moments I couldn't speak. I had never pried about his marriage or his wife, being quite content to live in the present and never anticipating there could be more. How obtuse I had been. How undiscerning and unreflective, wrapped up in my own little world, never giving a thought to what might be happening in his. Afraid to ask? Afraid of a new commitment? Well, now here it was. Out in the open and I had to say something.

The words fell out of my mouth before I'd even had time to consider them.

"Then come and live with me, darling."

His cry of gratitude was something I didn't deserve. I should have thought of this yonks ago.

"Oh, Laney! Do you mean it?"

"Of course I do. Come when you like. I don't know why I didn't think of it before. Didn't think it possible, I suppose."

So, a week later, when his wife had gone out for the afternoon, he arrived on my doorstep with all his clothes in six black bin bags.

"What have we done?" I asked, suddenly conscience-stricken when we'd stowed away all his things.

"Something we should have done years ago," he replied, opening a bottle of champagne. "You have no idea what you have rescued me from, Laney. Don't feel guilty about my wife. She should be feeling guilty about me and how unhappy she has made me for years. She is a difficult, unfeeling woman and I have hated her for a long time."

He poured the champagne and raised his glass, his face jubilant and looking ten years younger. "Here's to our happiness now. May it go on and on…"

But I still had to tell Syth, on whom I'd been so blithely cheating, and my heart quailed at the thought. How does one build happiness on the ruin of someone else's, especially someone who has done nothing to hurt you? He needed me more now than he had ever done and I was afraid of destroying him. The mere thought of what my defection would do to him made me feel sick. He was a lonely, vulnerable old man at the end of his life. He would suffer bitterly. He would give up and die and that would haunt me for the rest of my life. But there was Jim to think of now. Jim who had given up his marriage and risked the disapproval of all his friends to be with me. Something Syth had never been prepared to do. In any case, hadn't he told me some years back that if ever I found someone else he would accept it? I would have to tell him, screw my courage to the sticking place. There was no way round it.

But, coward that I was, I postponed my confession until Jim and I had had our first holiday together in Andalucia, where we had rented a farmhouse for three weeks.

The house stood high and remote on a mountain ridge overlooking a watch-towered bay and the small, whitewashed village of La Herradura on the coast of Granada province. It was run-down but roomy and comfortable and set in a glaucous green sea of avocado plantations and cherimoya orchards. There were views to the sea and, on a clear day, to Africa, from its vine-covered terrace, and an unruly garden with olive, orange and lemon trees, giant cactus and pink, red and purple bougainvillea. It was a perfect hideaway for us and I was impatient to be there with Jim.

"I'll tell Syth when we get back," I said.

Jim understood my apprehension. "I know you are unhappy about upsetting him. Would it help if I came with you when you tell him?"

"No, it's something I have to do myself."

"You don't have to ditch him entirely, you know. I understand how important he has been in your life. And I know how you hate the thought of hurting him. But you can still meet him for lunch when you like. I won't mind."

I was overwhelmed. "That is unbelievably generous!"

"I love you, too, Laney. I will do anything to make you happy."

"Perhaps we can all become friends?"

"Perhaps we can. We shall see."

But life is never that simple.

* * *

The telephone was ringing when we returned home. It was Syth. His voice, as rich and as mellifluous as ever, sent a pang through my heart. The thought of seeing him soon and hurting him was painful.

"Darling girl," he said and his voice was thick with emotion, "How nice to know you are back. I've missed you so much."

"I've missed you, too," I lied, guilty that I hadn't at all.

He cleared his throat nervously. "Darling, I'm afraid I can't meet you for lunch tomorrow as we'd arranged. I've been ill and in hospital for the last ten days and I'm not allowed out of the house. My daughter is here keeping an eye on me and I can't escape."

A tremor in my heart. The sense of an outer darkness closing.

"Oh Syth, sweetheart! What has happened?"

"It was my heart again. I filled up with water and my legs blew up twice their size. What a horrible experience that was."

I clung to the telephone burning with guilt because I'd been away when he'd needed me, and my imagination was running wild. Syth fighting for breath in a hospital bed, the valley of death opening up before him, while I had been in sexual abandon with someone else. I felt rotten. Sick of myself.

"Lena? Are you still there?"

"Yes, my dear. But I can hardly speak. It's such a shock."

"I'm much better now. The swelling has gone down and I am told I will be all right with strict rest. The only thing that devastates me is that strict rest means I won't be able to get out to see you. And I can't live without seeing you, Lena. There must be some way…"

His voice failed and I felt desperate. *Don't do this to us, God. Not yet. Please. Not yet.*

"You must concentrate on getting well, my darling. Don't fret about not being able to see me. It's far more important that you get better. I am here at the end of the telephone and we can talk every day. And if you want to see me – why, I can walk past your gate. If you come to your study window you can wave to me."

He was weeping pitifully and I felt enclosed in a dark cloud.

"Don't cry. Please don't cry!"

"Oh Lena! Is this what we have come to? You walking past my window? How can I bear seeing you walk past and not be able to hold you?"

"What else then?" I cried. "I can't think. I can't think."

There was a long silence at the other end of the telephone and then he said: "I've just had a thought. Perhaps we *can* meet. I have to be at the doctor's surgery the day after tomorrow. At noon. I shall have the car so we shall have somewhere to be alone together. Oh my darling, I long to see your dear face and to hold you."

"I will be there. Never fear."

And then it was my turn to break down, a squall of tears hitting me hard and blinding my eyes.

"Lena, please don't cry. I'm still here. Things will work out. They always have so why not this time? Don't lose faith in our guardian angels."

"I feel so terrible at having been away when you needed me." (Even worse at not having given him a thought in my happiness with Jim.)

"That's silly. You couldn't help it."

"Why didn't you ring me on my mobile? I'd have come home right away."

"I didn't want to worry you."

"But what if you'd died? How would I have felt at not having said goodbye?"

"Well, we don't have to say goodbye. I didn't die and have no intention of doing so just yet. So don't worry. Everything is going to be all right. Believe it."

It was raining the day I went to meet him: a sombre, dun-coloured day with lowering clouds spreading like bruises across a pallid sky. But I was too happy to care about the rain. The thought of seeing Syth again was a joyful one. He was still in the world and everything was as it should be. I looked forward to the loving smile that lifted his face whenever he saw me. I'd always felt redeemed by that smile. It made me feel I wasn't such a waste of space after all; for even making one person happy in the world is as good a reason as any for living.

I was at the surgery a few minutes before noon with presents for him from Spain: a bottle of Malaga wine, several bars of turron and a bottle of his favourite aftershave. I sat at the waiting room window, the easier to see him coming up the path. My spirits were high. I was grateful he was still on the planet. This business with Jim would have to wait a while until Syth was strong enough to take it. It would all work out somehow.

Noon came and went. Half an hour later he still hadn't appeared and I was the only person left in the waiting room. I approached the reception desk, my stomach in anxious knots.

"Can you tell me, please, if Mr Hardy has been in this morning? I arranged to meet him but may have mistaken the time."

The young, orange-haired receptionist checked her appointment book.

"The appointment was cancelled."

The knots tightened and I had a sharp sense of fate stringing his bow. I had to drag my voice from my boots.

"Have you any idea why it was cancelled?"

"No, I don't." An indifferent shrug.

"Then could you find out why, please?"

"Who are you? Are you a relative?" She sounded impatient, in a hurry to break for lunch.

Insolent cow! I'm his best friend, that's who. Much more important than any of his bloody relatives.

"I'm his niece," I said meekly. "We arranged to meet here at twelve."

"I'll make some inquiries," she said grudgingly and disappeared into one of the consulting rooms. When she returned her attitude was more conciliatory. Not surprising when she was about to slam the door in my face.

"I'm sorry. The gentleman died last night. He had a haemorrhage and his daughter took him to hospital. He died two hours later. Perhaps you should ring his home for more details."

* * *

In the weeks that followed I often wondered why I hadn't been aware of the moment he died. I should have been; should have known something was happening to him, should have had a sign, a clash of cymbals perhaps, an earth tremor, a nudge from the wind. How quietly our loved ones can slip away from us. How careless we can be with them.

It pained me deeply that I hadn't sensed him go. Of course, I had known it would happen sooner or later but I hadn't wanted to think about it. There had been plenty of intimations of the way it would be: his stroke, enlarged heart, increasing breathlessness. The inexorable descent into congestive heart failure had begun some time back. I had seen it but pushed it from my mind. A natural reaction, not wanting to look ahead. Few if any of us are prepared for the death of someone we love when it strikes. Nor for the disruption to life, the endless self-torment and the guilt at not having been as attentive as we should have been. I tormented myself silly because I hadn't been there for him when I had promised him I would be and because I'd been cheating on him.

Nor could I stop imagining his last moments... legs and belly bloated with fluid, open mouth gasping for air, deoxygenated lips and tongue turning blue. I imagined his eyes glazed with alarm, nostrils flaring with every attempt to breathe, excessive fluid damming his lungs, spilling through his body. Death by drowning in his own body fluids. God, why has dying to be so hard and ugly? Why do we have to die at all?

"Stop it, Laney," Jim said. "There is no point in endlessly speculating how it might have been. It was to be expected and has to be accepted. It's absurd of you to blame yourself for not having been there for him when it happened. How could you have known?"

"I'd promised I would be."

He pulled me close and stroked my hair. "Oh Laney, you can't keep every promise you make. Life doesn't work out that way. You made him happy and that's the best thing any human being can do for another. Now it's time for us to be happy. And we will be. I have never been more certain of anything in my life. We have to live now, Laney, as fully as we can."

I closed my eyes and leaned against his shoulder. I was so thankful he was there. But how long before jealous gods tore him away from me?

"Sometimes I am so afraid. I don't know that I can cope with any more death in my life. It seems to be dogging my footsteps. What if I should lose you?"

"You won't lose me, Laney. Not for a long time. What a way to think!"

He hugged me tightly. "Don't be afraid of committing yourself to love, Laney. It's all there is. All that counts."

Once we'd got all Jim's books, bookshelves and opera records moved over from his old home (and all the shirts he'd forgotten to bring with him when he left) I took early retirement to be with him and we embarked upon the best years of our lives. It seems a terrible thing to say but freed from my constant anxiety about Syth, I was able to at last commit fully to Jim who came to stand for everything in life that had any meaning. In the years that followed, I was to realise that rich harvest of happiness that Luis had forecast for me so many years back. So good to have someone all my own again.

And what a someone! How alike we were. What a lot we had in common and what a lot to talk about: favourite operas, best singers, best books, favourite paintings, favourite films. We were both into Fauve painting, Post-Impressionism, John Updike, Philip Roth, Cormac McCarthy, history, cricket, John Wayne westerns, *Dad's Army*, the *Carry On* movies. He was a great mimic, making me laugh until I got stomach ache. I had never laughed so much in all my life. What a release it was. And, of course, the more I laughed the wackier Jim got. Tommy Cooper, Max Wall, Terry Thomas, Frankie Howerd, Ken Dodd. I didn't know from one day to the next who would greet me.

One morning I woke up to find a Red Indian chief at the bedside, wrapped in a red and black Casa Pupo bedspread with a seagull feather in his hair. Another day it was Toulouse-Lautrec, tottering into the sitting room on his knees with my wide-brimmed black fedora on his head, a piece of black netting for a beard, a drawing book under one arm, a sweeping brush under the other. There was Long John Silver on a crutch with a black patch over one eye and a plastic parrot on his shoulder; Kermit the Frog with long green foam-rubber legs dangling from his sweater, and Santa Claus, every Christmas, jumping out at me from a walk-in cupboard in red pyjamas, a cotton wool beard and with a red towel on his head, going "Ho Ho Ho" all around the flat.

Jim was irrepressible. What a lot of fun I had been missing. What a lot of laughter. How fortunate I was to have got it right at last. And only just in time! All the loves in our lives serve an emotional purpose but there is only one great one and Jim was it. Mieciu may have been the first and most intense, but Jim and I were one. I had found my other half at last and with him complete happiness. When our years together ended I understood what Havelock Ellis meant when he wrote: 'The art of living is the art of loving.'

All right, so I was in it up to the neck again, loving so deeply that I'd be crucified if I lost him. But without an awareness of life's transience and the impermanence of all things how valuable would life be? Without risk there would be no gain. Without sadness we would all dry up.

We'd been together a year when Al died. It was unexpected but not unhappy. She had not been ill. She died in her sleep after a hard day's work in the garden and I was relieved she had escaped the worst depredations of dying, like those that my mother had endured with breast cancer two years before.

"I've had a good life," Al told me a few weeks previously when she had been staying with us in Edinburgh. "I'm tired and ready to go. Life is such a restless dream I would hate to think of it going on forever. A bit of repose will be quite nice. I'm not worried. Especially now that I see you happy and settled with someone to take care of you. I didn't like you living alone. It's not much fun."

"That's what you did," I reminded her gently. "Was it so bad?"

"I didn't think so at the time but watching you and Jim together, always so close, so integrated, so loving, I realise I've missed out. I'm envious. I've never known it that way with anyone."

"I wasted a lot of years clinging to father figures, didn't I? But they were what I wanted at the time and they worked. But they were unequal loves: Mieciu was my Svengali, Syth the quiet protector. Jim and I are the same generation. Equals. Similar backgrounds, similar upbringing, similar education, the same way of looking at the world. He fills my heart every hour of every day and I know I fill his. I hope we can have a long, long time together."

"It's a tragedy you didn't find each other sooner."

"Yes, and if I lose him I shall be annihilated."

"Ach! That's no way to think in the midst of your happiness. Why spoil the present with gloomy thoughts about the future? All you can do is live each day as fully as possible and store the memories away for recollection on the rainy days to come."

She was right. It was the only way to live and I began to keep a diary, recording every day Jim and I spent together, what we said, what we did, where we went, what we laughed about. Living with him was bliss and I realised how long it had been since I'd lived with a man and how much I'd been missing. He was sweetness itself to me: generous, tender, good-humoured and wise. He brought me tea to bed in the mornings, cooked lunch if I wanted to spend a day painting, wiped the smudges of paint from my face and hair and from all the taps and doorknobs where I'd been with my painty fingers.

He tinted my hair, tweezed stray whiskers from my chin, found my specs whenever I mislaid them, painted my toe nails, cleaned out the juicer which was something I hated, cooked fish the way I liked it – very crisp – made a fair dish of mince and tatties, and often knelt in the street to tie my shoelaces which were always coming undone.

"What a little girl you are. Didn't anyone teach you to tie your laces properly?"

I felt such a rush of love for him at times that I thought I would faint. Even the most ordinary aspects of life were gilded just because he was there. I loved to watch him showering, shaving, taking a leak, doing his morning exercises in his tanga briefs, dancing a few naked pirouettes for my delight before tumbling into bed at night. It was great to fall asleep with my legs around him, my cheek nestling in the hollow between his shoulder blades, his testicles in the palm of my hand, to wake up mornings to his sweet warmth and his towering penis: "See what you do to me, Laneypies?"

"You are a banquet for my hungry eyes, my lovely one. Come here and let me sup."

"Laney, I was never so happy with anyone as I am with you. We should have got together sooner. But there it is, you stick with a lousy marriage because you don't know how different life can be. Not until someone like you comes along and lights up the whole world. Suddenly you know that this is the woman you want to be with day and night for the rest of your life. And to know she feels the same way! What riches!"

My heart soared. Of course I felt the same way. How could I not? He was beautiful to me and I hated being away from him even to go to the corner shop or to have my hair done. I adored everything about him and I loved everything we did together: our siestas on the sofa on wintry afternoons followed by tea and crumpets in front of the fire; the baths we took together; the wet Sundays we stayed in bed reading the papers and taking it in turns to make the bacon sandwiches; the days we spent glued to the television set watching Test cricket; the sunny Saturday afternoons we spent over at the Carlton Cricket Club watching matches; the long walks along the sea shore at Aberlady or Yellowcraigs; picking blackberries along the river out at South Queensferry; the evenings sitting companionably side by side reading books; holding hands in the back row at the Filmhouse, dashing over to Lazio's afterwards for a pizza.

Funny how simple things can acquire such a lustre when you do them with your soulmate.

But there are hazards to love round every corner. He was not strong, his body having taken quite a beating over the years: half his stomach removed because of an ulcer, his gallbladder gone, two heart bypasses which necessitated his having to take warfarin and digoxin for the rest of his life. The deeper my love grew so, too, my anxiety for him. I began to panic at signs of fragility: if he caught a cold or had a headache, if he looked pale.

Such anxiety is the other side of the coin of love but would human beings love so intensely if they knew they were going to live for ever?

Aware of my fears, he would laugh them off. "Don't fret, Laney. I'm quite tough you know."

But it was hard not to fret. It was too perfect to last. Sooner or later Fate would make a move to destroy what we had and the grief would begin. It's the price we pay when we choose the path of love, when we dare to be happy. I understood that well enough. Just didn't want to pay up for a long, long time.

***

When the blow fell we were out in Andalucia. He had been subdued for a few weeks, all the liveliness gone out of him, and I hadn't heard him singing for a long while.

"Darling, are you all right? It's not like you to be so quiet."

"I'm just a bit weary. Anno Domini, I guess. And I have a pain behind my left knee that's been bothering me a while. I hope it's not the old gout problem coming back. I've had enough of that."

"Perhaps you should see the doctor before we go away?"

"No. I have my gout pills with me. Don't worry. It will wear off. Let's get out to Spain and lie in the sun. That will do me more good than anything else."

But after three weeks in Spain the pain in his leg worsened and began to drive him frantic. And when his whole leg swelled and he couldn't put his foot down on the ground without screaming, I knew we were in big trouble and sent for the doctor.

"A thrombosis," he said immediately. "He will have to go to hospital for treatment. They will dissolve the clot and he should be out in five or six days."

He was in hospital eight days, lying with his feet up, forbidden to get out of bed, and I stayed with him day and night, sleeping on a reclining chair beside his bed. I was there to wash him down, hold the urine bottle for him, struggle with the bed pan. I hurt for his hurt and for his hurt pride – at my having to wipe his bottom.

"Oh darling, what a comedown. What am I doing to you?"

"It's nothing, silly. I love you. I love everything about you. Even your anus. It's rather sweet: small and pink like a rosebud. Can I kiss it?"

He couldn't help laughing. "Laney, you're incorrigible!"

The doctors dissolved the clot but never asked how it had come about in a man whose blood was too thin to clot because of the warfarin he was on. And we were only too eager to be free of the hospital and get back to Scotland to ask. The medics let him go with a caution to go easy and walk only a few steps a day.

"A week will do," Jim said. "A week's rest here, some short walks, and then perhaps we can get home."

"I'll get you back somehow, my lovely lad. Even if we have to hire a taxi all the way back to Edinburgh. But we have to be very careful. I'm not listening to you any more. Don't you realise what a risk you were taking not to let me call a doctor sooner? You could have had a massive stroke and not be here now."

"Don't go on at me, Laney, or I shall burst into tears."

I wanted to burst into tears, too, and seeing the struggle on my face he reached for me.

"It's going to be all right, Laney. Trust me. I'll get better. There's no way I am going to leave you."

Back at our mountain hideaway we walked a little in the garden and stood for a while on the terrace watching swifts and house martins, myriads of them, falling with shrill delight on the evening midges. My lovely lad, looking pale and gaunt and clinging tremulously to a couple of walking sticks, did a brief turn across the lawn and back, spindly legs shaking under him.

"It's so good to be out of that hospital," he said. "Now I have to get strong enough to travel home."

Looking at him I felt myself disintegrating and was filled with foreboding. He looked so frail it would take weeks to get him strong enough to endure a plane journey.

"Come to me, my little skinamalink. Let me hold you and keep you safe. I love you so much, so much. You are all I want. Please don't leave me."

He sighed and quivered in my arms and I experienced a stab of fear. I've been here before, I thought, remembering Mieciu and the radiance that was in his face a few days before he died. That radiance was in Jim's face now. We were on the knife edge.

"How ugly I am now," he said sadly. "Just an old bonebag now."

"Ugly? You? Oh no, my lovely lad, you can never be ugly. You are truly beautiful, shimmering with a life that illuminates me, too."

He managed a wry laugh and kissed me gently. "What a poet! Never mind, Laney. We are being tested but we'll get through it. In a week or two I'll be back making love like a buck rabbit."

"Of course you will, my love," I whispered. But I didn't give a damn if he never made love to me again. All I wanted was for him to live, live, LIVE. For without him there was no life for me.

That night I made poignant love to him, insisting that he remain quite still while I caressed him all over and took him into my mouth. He lay silent as I loved him, eyes tight shut against the tears that were quivering beneath his lashes, and afterwards I licked the tears away thinking how beautiful he was, ethereal and as finely-wrought as porcelain.

"Don't chicken out on me. I can't go on living without you. I can't live only half a person and that's what I shall be without you."

"I'll try not to, sweet Laney."

But he was already on the road away from me even as he spoke and when I woke next morning it was to find him sitting up in bed with a white, frightened face.

"Laney," he said, reaching out to me. "I can't see anything. I've gone blind."

My body shook from top to toe.

"Oh No! Oh No! Oh No!" I shouted. "Not this. Not like this."

I turned his face to mine. "Look at me, Jimbly. Look. How many fingers am I holding up?"

His eyes were expressionless. All light flown.

"Darling," he said softly. "I can't even see your lovely face."

I leapt out of bed, threw on some clothes and started repacking the suitcase I had so thankfully emptied the night before. I was terrified. Frantic. I kept saying, "Oh God, Oh God, Oh God," over and over again and my heart was like lead.

"Don't panic," he said.

But my mind was a blur of panic. I could hardly see what I was doing for panic. My limbs were almost numb with it. And if I felt like that what in God's name was Jim feeling?

"We must get back to the hospital. Fast. It could be something to do with the thrombosis. I've heard this can sometimes cause a temporary loss of sight." (Had I really heard that or was I just making it up to encourage him?)

"Let's pray you're right, Laney. Let's pray for all we're worth."

But prayer was a waste of time. A scan at the hospital showed a secondary prostate cancer tumour on the brain. This, a kindly doctor explained, would account for the thrombosis because cancer tumours threw off blood clots.

He looked at me sympathetically and made me sit down.

"There is no hope," he said. "The tumour will encroach on everything and all we can do for him now is to keep him comfortable on oxygen and morphine. It is what I would do for any of my family in the same situation."

I stumbled back to the ward. Sledgehammered. Vomit rising. I reached Jim's bedside and stood there wordless and choking on tears.

Sensing me beside him, Jim reached out for me.

"Is that you, Laney?"

"Yes, I'm here."

I sat down on his bed and took his hands in mine. They were beautiful feminine hands, long-fingered and slender. I held them to my lips and kissed them over and over until they were wet with my tears.

"Calm down, Laney," he said softly. "Calm down. Take your time and tell me. It's bad news isn't it?"

I don't remember what I said or how I found the words. All I could recall later was the ghost-whiteness of his waif-like face, the tightness of his lips, the resignation in his eyes and my own sobs of terror that came leaping like frogs out of my mouth.

"Lie beside me," he said. "Hold me."

And I climbed up onto the bed and lay beside him, my head on his pillow, my fingers caressing his face. We lay there all afternoon and all through the night, his body growing heavier against me. I mopped his sweating brow with a small hand towel and gave him sips of water from a paper cup. And I couldn't stop kissing him. Kissing and kissing and kissing because the time of kisses was almost past.

"You're a brave girl. It wasn't easy to tell me."

"It would have been wrong not to."

Years back when Mieciu was dying of cancer no-one had wanted to tell him. Not even the doctors. "It might lessen his will to hang on," they said. And I'd complied because I was young and didn't know better and because, in those days, death was not a permissible piece of knowledge. I know now how wrong that was. For what is the point in giving people false hope? The truth enables them to prepare for death and to say proper goodbyes to those they love.

The prostate cancer was a huge shock.

"I didn't suspect a thing," Jim said. "I didn't feel very good but apart from the pain in my leg there was nothing I could put my finger on."

He sighed heavily. "What a bastard thing," he said in such a blighted voice that I began to cry again.

"Hush now, Laney," he whispered, his hand feeling for my face to caress it. "It doesn't help anything to cry so. You can't turn the clock back, no matter how many tears you shed for me. You must be brave."

"I want to come with you," I wailed. "Life isn't worth going on with if I don't have you beside me. You are my reason for living."

"And you have been mine, Laney, and I feel like weeping because I'm abandoning you and I don't want to."

"Would you go on if you lost me? If it was the other way round?"

"Of course I would. There is no alternative. Don't think of doing anything silly. You have to stick it out. Be strong. For my sake."

The next day I washed him down from head to toe, dismayed at how rattleboned he had become, how translucent his skin, how meagre his thighs. I caressed his penis, so small and sad now, thinking of its more swashbuckling times and all the pleasure it had given me.

He was startled. "Hey! What are you up to?"

"Just stroking you, my love. You are achingly beautiful."

"They were good times weren't they, Laney?"

"Sublime, my sweet."

"Especially our candlemasses."

Candlemass was our term for making love with the bed surrounded by candles. Red candles. Above the bed, beside the bed, on all the shelves, bedside tables and the dressing table. They cast a womb-like glow over the room and purple shadows on our bodies.

"Especially those," I said, heart cracking all over like old china.

"I don't want to leave you, darling."

104

Speechless, I buried my face in the hollow of his neck.

"We had it all, Laney. We have been lucky, luckier than most. We may have come late to love but the main thing is we found it eventually. And we have been happy, haven't we?"

"In every way, Jimblypies. You have filled my heart to overflowing. You always will. Until my last breath I shall love you."

"It's been a whole new world with you, Laney. The happiest days of my life."

"Mine, too," I said quietly, thinking, *never a mean or a cross word, never a disappointment, complete trust always.*

"We are part of each other, Laney. Two of a kind. We know each other inside out and that is how it should be. Sometimes it feels as if we are twin souls."

And if he dies I shall no longer be because he will take my soul with him.

"Please, please don't go. I need you. Without you I shall be nothing. I won't be able to bear life without you."

"I shall still be part of you, Laney. Watching over everything you do. Our love won't end just because I'm moving on to some other place. I shall always be with you. Believe it."

Two nights before he died he suffered a pulmonary embolism, his heart going berserk, like a small animal trying to leap out of his chest. I was terrified as he thrashed around in pain, sweat streaming from him, saturating his pyjama jacket. He was hot, temperature soaring, and pleading in a faraway voice that shredded my heart: "Let's go home. Let's go home."

"Soon," I said. "Soon, my darling."

A nurse came and gave him a shot of something to calm him down and for a couple of hours he drifted quietly in my arms.

Around midnight, wrenching himself from his misery, he said firmly: "Laney, it's time to say goodbye. I have to go. There are too many problems. I'm seizing up and can't move.

Don't cry. Don't look back. No regrets. Be brave and don't be afraid. There's nothing to be afraid of. I promise I shall haunt you. I shall be watching over everything you do."

His voice faltered. "Laney, I worship you. I have always worshipped you."

They were his last words to me and stunned and desolate I held him, half in my mind and half out of it, thinking how in a short while it would be as if he had never existed, and how could that be? In a while I would be searching the crowded streets for him, wake in the night and reach in vain for him. Never again in my life would I hear his soft voice, his laughter, his songs, feel his kisses. I couldn't get my mind around it. Saw the abyss of sorrow and loneliness opening up again and felt only utter weariness.

"My dear, sweet, most lovely lad," I whispered. "You have been the world to me." And I began kissing him frantically, kissing his poor frayed face and thrusting my tongue between his cooling lips, plundering his mouth for the last faint drops of his life.

To my amazement and, yes, exhilaration even on the edge of death, he responded with heartrending eagerness. He was still in there, unable to see, unable to speak, unable to move, but still very much aware of me and giving me kisses as deep and as searching as my own.

Those last dying kisses will haunt me for the rest of my life. They had welled up from the depths of his imprisoned soul and were branded forever on mine. They were his last gift to me.

* * *

How hard it is to start again! I had done it before, I know, but I was weary of making the effort. God was playing some ugly game with me. Three loved ones dead was wanton cruelty. I'd had more than enough and no longer wished to stay on the planet.

Wasn't it Nietzsche who said that anyone with a purpose could survive anything? Well, I no longer had a purpose. Jim had been the hard centre to my life, my soulmate. I'd been travelling all my life towards him only to have him snatched so callously from me. Gone forever the most beautiful creature in the universe, my lean and graceful best of loves: in his tawny eyes the shades of bracken; in his voice the soft ripple of dark Scottish burns; in his generous heart adoration for me. Happy as I had been with my father figures I hadn't known until Jim that completeness, that sense of oneness with another being that Plato talked about. Life would never be as good as that again, nor I so lucky.

A year after his death depression and anomie were setting in and thoughts of suicide grew sharper. It made sense. I'd had the best – why wait for some dread disease to twist my body or dementia to shrivel my brain? If there was even the slightest chance of finding him again in another dimension then why not go looking for him now? And I wouldn't give up until I'd turned over every damned star in the universe.

So I bought a book about suicide called *Final Exit* and was surprised at the number of ways open to me. There was hanging, cyanide, drowning, razoring one's veins, car exhaust, sleeping pills with a plastic bag over one's head (although you have to remember to take an anti-sickness pill first or you vomit everything back again). Best of all it seemed to me was lying out on a mountain side one frosty night. I liked the idea of freezing under the stars. And I wouldn't have far to go to do it. The cemetery across the road would do. I'd take thirty sleeping pills and lie down on one of the stone benches and keep my eyes on the stars until I fell asleep. The moon would cast its pale shroud over me... the dawn chorus would be better than a church choir.

But first I had a promise to keep. This was to leave some of Jim's ashes at the heart of an old carob tree in the mountains of southern Spain. It was a favourite place. One where we had often picnicked and made love. And although he hadn't asked for it, I'd had a small brass plaque engraved to fix to the tree trunk. This was to let the passing world know that one James Mercer Ritchie had existed. Not that he'd have cared about the world but I felt the need for witnesses, hating the thought of someone as vibrant as he simply squandered on the wind.

The decision to return was not easy. Andalucia was where he had died and I had sworn never again to set foot in Spain. But, one day, there I was, on a borrowed Honda 250cc motorbike rattling up the track to the ridge where the carob stood like Atlas shouldering the sky.

One afternoon when we were lying beside the tree, Jim had said: "I love this place, Laney. I love looking down on the Med and over to Africa. It's like being on top of the world. When I die will you scatter a few of my ashes here? Of course I want most of them scattered at home in Edinburgh but a smidgeon here would be very nice."

And clambering a little way up the carob, he pointed to a deep crevice at the heart of the tree. "Right here will do. Then, when you come back here you won't feel so alone because part of me will be here with you. If you look closely enough you might even find my face hiding in the leaves."

I couldn't reply. My heart had wilted. That he would leave me was a possibility too terrible to contemplate. With him I was complete and the thought of life without him shrivelled my heart. Perhaps, like the wife in the film *The Hairdresser's Husband* I should kill myself at the height of our rapture. But how would I know when the summit had been reached? I was always on a high with him. It would be difficult to know the right moment because I'd be thinking, "Just one more week. One more month. One more year."

And then it was too late. He had beaten me to it, leaving me with only ashes in a blue and white ceramic pot and memories that burned me up night and day. I was sick of it. Sick of the loneliness and the tight, painful knot of anguish always there beneath my ribs and there was no fight left in me.

"Life is worth going on with provided you are not in pain," he'd said.

Well, I *was* in pain. And it *wasn't* all right without him and never would be. He had gone, taking with him all my past, present and future, all the fullness and richness of my life. The dance was ended, the roses deadheaded and I was old and in the abyss with a 9/11-size hole where my heart should be. I had loved him to bits and his death had left me in bits, all burned out, fuses blown and determined to put an end to the heartache that would otherwise dog me for the rest of my days.

After scattering the ashes and nailing up the plaque, I was going to do a 'Thelma and Louise' and drive myself off the end of the ridge and into oblivion.

I opened the throttle wide to tackle the steepening road. It was late afternoon on the coast of Granada province: close on five and the sun beginning to soften and blue shadows lengthen in the valley. A warm wind mussed my hair and I felt a bittersweet happiness as I flashed past all the places that had meant so much to us: the olive grove where rivers of poppies clamoured every May for us to paint them; the spring where a midwife toad, the size of a dinner plate, spent its days; the copse where a nightingale improvised day and night; the old fox den; bee eaters' corner, as noisy and as flashy as ever; Antonio's cottage where we'd sometimes shared the old man's midday meal of crusty bread, broad beans and his own rough red wine.

Pajarito had been alive then – Antonio's ancient mule. Always nuzzling at my trouser pocket for the Treble X mints I kept there for him. If I fed him three at a time he had an erection as big as a baseball bat.

"Don't be silly!" Jim laughed when I mentioned the baseball bat. "It's not the mints that are such a hit. It's you, Laneypies. I know so because you have the same effect on me. And that's without the mints!"

A picture of him naked and wanting flashed into my mind and my heart lurched. *Oh my lovely, loving lad! So sweet and tender and true. How lucky I was to have been alive with you.*

I sped on up the hill, past the shrine to the Virgin of Fatima where we'd joined villagers at its opening party; past the bamboo thicket where Pajarito had fallen down a hole and had to be hauled out by tractor; skirted the thickset prickly pear that tumbled in an unruly cataract down the ridge; and, rounding the bend by the ruined farmhouse, was out on the ridge top and bumping along the goat tracks towards the carob. It stood at the end of the ridge, on a rocky escarpment that fell sharply to the valley floor. It was a monumental presence. I'd forgotten what a colossus it was, how voluminous its foliage, how massive its girth. Three hundred years old with at least another three hundred years to go. Now that's a life.

Propping the motorbike against an olive tree, I approached the carob and my heart was full for this was where we had often sat and painted, me with my slapdash acrylics, Jim with his delicate oil pastels.

"Hello Ancient One," I said, and throwing my arms around the tree trunk stood for a while with my forehead pressed against the warm bark, trying to absorb some of the tree's tremendous life force. I felt in great need of some of that strength.

After a few moments I scrambled up the trunk until I could reach the cleft where Jim had wanted me to leave some ashes. I had screws and a small screwdriver with me, fixed the plaque and then emptied a matchboxful of ashes into the fissure. Several splinters of bone fell out and my heart snagged and cracked again. So many cracks now, I thought, I'm surprised it hasn't fallen apart.

Close to tears and shaking, I clambered down again and read the inscription on the plaque aloud: "In memory of James Mercer Ritchie who loved this place and was loved by me. He was beautiful and we had it all. Marlena Frick."

Another gust of emotion ransacked my heart. With him everything had come together and I knew that I had been travelling towards him all along. Mieciu had opened the doors to my future. Syth had sustained me after Mieciu died. With Jim I had reached completion. One flesh. One mind. One heart. I was on the planet to love Jim Ritchie. It was preordained.

Of course he hadn't wanted to go. It had been wonderful for him, too.

"The best years of my life with you, Laney. A whole new world. No regrets. Be glad for what we have known and grateful that we found each other. Think how easily we could have passed each other by."

"That isn't much consolation now I'm going to lose you."

He smiled, his face creasing into the dozens of little lines that I loved so much.

"I'll wait for you, Laney, if it's allowed. With you I have had so much more than I ever dared imagine. Just let anybody try to stop me from finding you again."

A little moan escaped my lips as I stood there, trembling, on the ridge. I read the plaque again and tears sprang in my eyes.

"Don't look back," he'd said. But how could I not look back when the past was all I had? And what was the point in surviving without him when he had been the light of my life?

Time to put an end to all this sadness, I thought. Time to do the 'Thelma and Louise' stunt. It might be quite something to soar off the scarp and tumble down that gilded sky. To be or not to be was a question that had nagged at me for a long time. Now

I was decided. There had to be an end to all the heartache. Now or never.

It was then I saw the eagle heading straight for me across the cloudless sky. I watched it idly, thinking it would pass on overhead but I was wrong. It stopped right above the carob, hovering so low on the thermals I could see the white feathers in its ringed tail. A golden eagle. A young bird. A newly-hatched spirit.

I drew a sharp breath and watched as the bird began several slow, lazy circles above the tree. It did this ten or eleven times and, counting, I felt irradiated, altered somehow, neurons firing wildly, blood racing with the expectancy of a divine revelation, nostrils filled with the scent of roses where no roses grew.

Surely this was a sign? Why else out of this vast, rucked-up land of countless ridges and thousands of carob trees would this imperious bird have swept down from the sierra to circle above the tree where I had just scattered some of my beloved's ashes?

"Jim!" I shouted. "My love, oh my love, is it you?"

Well, of course it was! Any old American Indian could have told me that.

The eagle swooped lower, watching me, and then turned back towards the sierra. Panic rose in my throat.

"No, no! Don't go! Please come back Jim, please come back!"

And to my astonishment, the bird returned to etch one last circle in the sky and in that moment I was aware of being outside myself, of looking down at myself beside the tree. It was a weird sensation, a transient experience lasting only a few seconds perhaps, but a moment of connection so vivid it will stay with me for the rest of my life.

Enthralled, I waited until the bird was out of sight and then I sank to my knees and began to weep. In that brief, heady moment it seemed I had been blessed by a benign force and overwhelmed. I wept and wept and wondered if I would ever stop.

But this time my tears were different from the maudlin, self-pitying ones that had dogged me since Jim died. These were cleansing tears, tears of release and of hope, for the quality of that encounter with the eagle had lifted my heart somewhere beyond the stars, the sense of being connected to something 'other' so vivid that I felt deeply reassured.

It's difficult to convey the soaring rapture of that experience and the quality of calm that descended on me afterwards. But that glimpse of universal harmony I experienced was real enough. It was one of those moments that can flare up when you are listening to great music, absorbed in nature, or deeply, deeply happy. Something in the moment triggers a joyous awakening of what seems to be a second self. You want to shout, "Yes! Yes!" And then the moment is gone. We can't hold it. But we can remember it and keep it always in the forefront of our minds for what else can these moments of grace be but pointers to something transcendent? They are so restorative, their significance at the time so clear and unambiguous, we would be foolish to dismiss them merely as tricks of the mind. They are moments outside the ordinary patterns of existence, a few seconds only that may not be evidence of the 'otherness' we all seek but which should not be lightly dismissed because none of us can know what possibilities may lie beyond the present limits of human knowledge.

Eventually, wept dry, I lay back against the warm tree trunk, closed my eyes and drifted into sleep. I was thinking of how good it had been with us and of the joyous times we had spent together here on the ridge where we had often made the hump-backed creature of love under the stars, in the copper glow of a late afternoon, once even in the rain.

When I awoke it was to a red horizon and magenta clouds and an oceanic feeling of complete tranquillity and unity with the universe. A change had occurred. I knew it as soon as I opened my eyes. I heard Jim's voice in my head saying, as he had said on his deathbed: "There is nothing to be afraid of." And I knew that he was right.

Feeling uplifted and energised, I stood up and crossed to the Honda, sitting astride it for a while absorbing the serene ending of the day, watching a burnished copper sun sinking into a violet sea, gilding the edges of the wind-flattened clouds, and turning the mountainous land rubiate.

A warm breeze, censed with pine and rosemary and a hint of wood smoke, drifted upwards through the valley and with it the song of a nightingale roused from the torpor of a dog-day afternoon.

So much beauty in the world, I thought. It hurts without the one you love to share it but it can also heal if you let it, if you can hold on to it. For it opens one's sensibilities to a higher reality. Surely there was enough comfort in that to live on?

"We had it all," I said loudly. "We had it all and it can never get better than that."

Sighing, I gave the bike a kick start. Hell, I wasn't the only person in the world to be grieving for a lost love. There were thousands out there like me struggling to make sense of it all and find a path up through the loneliness and out of the void. And there were thousands more who would eventually tread the same path.

Slowly I let out the clutch and turned my back on the whole 'Thelma and Louise' option, thinking what a criminal waste it would have been of all the love that had been invested in me.

I felt serene, almost happy, as I sped down again to the sea. Something had been accomplished. I had accepted grief and, having accepted it, would ride life out a day at a time… with as much grace as I could muster.

When I was young and in love for the very first time, I never dreamt that it could end, never gave a thought to the fact that everything changes, that everything existing on this planet is born to die. I was in love, basking in the blissful ignorance of youth, believing my love to be unique and that it would last forever. It was only when Mieciu lay dead in my arms that I became aware of the worm at the root of everything.

From then on I have known the anxiety that smoulders continually beneath all our happiest moments, the heartache of loving someone you know you will lose sooner or later, whose body will disintegrate, strength decline, beauty fade, eyes grow pale, warmth grow cold. I grew up, understanding at last that all things are mutable and that not even the grandest passion is defence against this.

But I have also learned that life is all the sweeter for this underlying angst and am grateful for all the sweetness I have known. It takes courage to make oneself vulnerable to love for it can wound and is the source of suffering. Some people deliberately shut themselves away from it in order to avoid the pain and who can blame them? But private space is a lonely country and not for me.

I have known happiness, a lot of it, in a world where unhappiness is endemic; fortunate to have known love when so many people do not, privileged to have known the quiet joy, the inner peace and confidence that comes with finding oneself in the right place with the right person.

Yes, such joy brings fear with it; the terror, in fact, of eventual loss. But that fear also enhances the value of what we have and prompts us to take more care of those we love, intensifying their happiness and, in so doing, redoubling our own. And, eventually, when we lose them, there is great comfort to be had in knowing that we did our best for them. How fortunate we are that we can conjure up happy memories with loved ones in this way. How fortunate that we have had loved ones at all. Nor are they really dead. Not when we can bring them to mind so easily.

Some people will say I have been a beggar for love. I don't doubt it. But aren't we all looking for love? And what's wrong with that? It seems to me it is only in the act of loving that we redeem ourselves and enrich our lives and the lives of others. When I look back on my own sweet lost loves I see how each one has illumined my life and shaped my existence and I am grateful. Through them I have learned the value of commitment, the demands of loyalty, the pleasure of giving and of being given to, the joy of life shared with a like mind, the tenderness of men, the value of compassion, the pathos of old age, the desolation but also the fortitude and inner grace of the dying.

These are valuable lessons. Because of them my heart is richly-lined and strong.

In one of his moments of torment, Jim cried out: "Set me free! Set me free!" His cry rent my heart and I longed to be able to prise apart his rib cage and release his frantic spirit. In that moment I had a strong sense of a soul clamouring to escape from a body no longer able to protect it and an intense awareness of the energy of which Jim was composed, massing ready for flight.

I remember wondering if energy could die and who on earth or in heaven was Jim pleading with because it certainly wasn't me.

Later, when he was calmer and out of pain, I asked if he had found peace.

"Yes, Laney," he said. "The peace that passeth all understanding."

Well, how could I complain about that? I had to let it go at that and be glad for him no matter how much I was hurting inside.

I am someone more than I was because of all this love and loss and even though the damage to my heart is forever I can live more easily with the scars because I have loved well and been well loved on this earth. This is enough. This is more than enough.

Epilogue

If you find one day
what is left of me
is old and dry
and crossword-puzzle
the only game
that I still can play
in bed at night,
come to my lips
with a kiss of life.

Donald Clarke